YORK NOTES

THE SIGN OF THE FOUR

ARTHUR CONAN DOYLE

WORKBOOK BY LYN LOCKWOOD

The right of Lyn Lockwood to be identified as the Author of this Work
has been asserted by her in accordance with the Copyright,
Designs and Patents Act 1988

YORK PRESS
322 Old Brompton Road, London SW5 9JH

PEARSON EDUCATION LIMITED
Edinburgh Gate, Harlow,
Essex CM20 2JE, United Kingdom
Associated companies, branches and representatives throughout the world

First published 2018

10 9 8 7 6 5 4 3 2 1

ISBN 978–1–2922–3686–5

Illustrations by John Rabou; and Alan Batley (page 48 only)

Phototypeset by Swales and Willis Ltd
Printed in Slovakia

Photo credits: Bikeworldtravel/Shutterstock for page 13 / kahksha siddiqui/Shutterstock
for page 14 / Jess Wealleans/Shutterstock for page 18 / Stepan Bormotov/Shutterstock
for page 20 / Rigamondis/Shutterstock for page 26 / TTStock/Shutterstock for
page 27 / dkART/Shutterstock for page 40 / XiXinXing/iStock for
page 43 / hanssiergers/iStock for page 46 / pederk/iStock for page 55

CONTENTS

PART ONE:
GETTING STARTED

PART TWO:
PLOT AND ACTION

PART THREE:
CHARACTERS

PART FOUR:
THEMES, CONTEXTS AND SETTINGS

PART FIVE:
FORM, STRUCTURE AND LANGUAGE

PART SIX:
PROGRESS BOOSTER

PART ONE: GETTING STARTED

Preparing for assessment

HOW WILL I BE ASSESSED ON MY WORK ON *THE SIGN OF THE FOUR*?

The Sign of the Four is set by AQA only and your work will be examined through these three Assessment Objectives:

Assessment Objectives	Wording	Worth thinking about ...
A01	Read, understand and respond to texts. Students should be able to: • maintain a critical style and develop an informed personal response • use textual references, including quotations, to support and illustrate interpretations.	• How well do I know what happens, what people say, do, etc? • What do I think about the key ideas in the novella? • How can I support my viewpoint in a really convincing way? • What are the best quotations to use and when should I use them?
A02	Analyse the language, form and structure used by a writer to create meanings and effects, using relevant subject terminology where appropriate.	• What specific things does the writer 'do'? What choices has Conan Doyle made? (Why this particular word, phrase or paragraph here? Why does this event happen at this point?) • What effects do these choices create? Suspense? Mystery? Humour?
A03	Show understanding of the relationships between texts and the contexts in which they were written.	• What can I learn about society from the novella? (What does it tell me about attitudes towards people from other cultures in Conan Doyle's day, for example?) • What was society like in Conan Doyle's time? Can I see it reflected in the text?

Look out for the Assessment Objective labels throughout your York Notes Workbook – these will help to focus your study and revision!

The text used in this Workbook is the Collins Classic edition, 2015.

How to use your York Notes Workbook

There are lots of ways your Workbook can support your study and revision of *The Sign of the Four*. There is no 'right' way – choose the one that suits your learning style best.

1) Alongside the York Notes Study Guide and the text	2) As a 'stand-alone' revision programme	3) As a form of mock-exam
Do you have the York Notes Study Guide for *The Sign of the Four*? The contents of your Workbook are designed to match the sections in the Study Guide, so with the novella to hand you could: • read the relevant section(s) of the Study Guide and any part of the novella referred to; • complete the tasks in the same section in your Workbook.	Think you know *The Sign of the Four* well? Why not work through the Workbook systematically, either as you finish chapters, or as you study or revise certain aspects in class or at home. You could make a revision diary and allocate particular sections of the Workbook to a day or week.	Prefer to do all your revision in one go? You could put aside a day or two and work through the Workbook, page by page. Once you have finished, check all your answers in one go! This will be quite a challenge, but it may be the approach you prefer.

HOW WILL THE WORKBOOK HELP YOU TEST AND CHECK YOUR KNOWLEDGE AND SKILLS?

Parts Two to **Five** offer a range of tasks and activities:

These fun and quick-to-complete tasks check your basic knowledge of the text.

These more open questions challenge you to show your understanding.

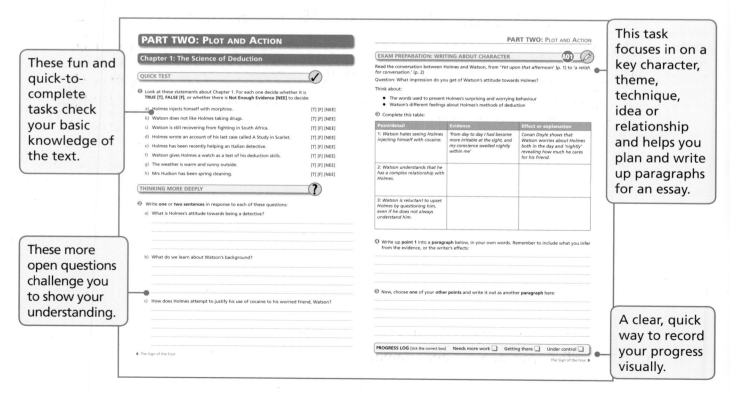

This task focuses in on a key character, theme, technique, idea or relationship and helps you plan and write up paragraphs for an essay.

A clear, quick way to record your progress visually.

Each Part ends with a **Practice task** to extend your revision:

An exam-style task is provided at the end of each section for you to practise a full essay.

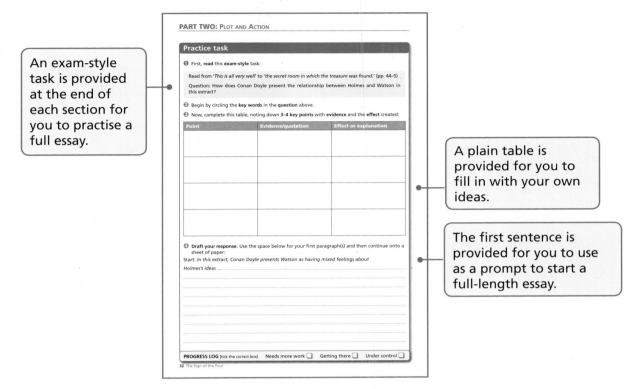

A plain table is provided for you to fill in with your own ideas.

The first sentence is provided for you to use as a prompt to start a full-length essay.

Part Six: Progress Booster helps you test your own key writing skills:

A sample of a student's writing challenges you to judge its strengths and weaknesses.

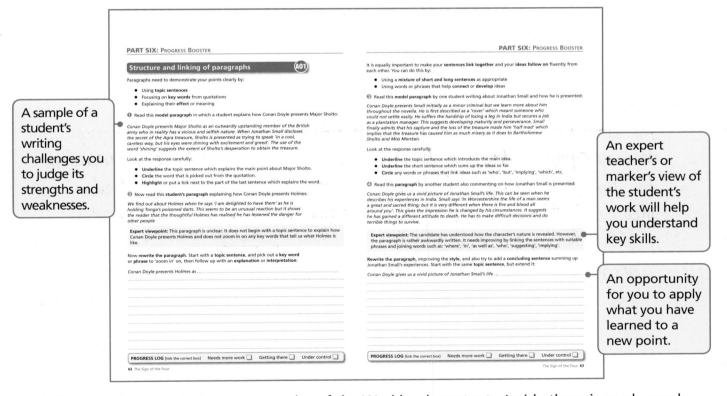

An expert teacher's or marker's view of the student's work will help you understand key skills.

An opportunity for you to apply what you have learned to a new point.

Don't forget – these are just some examples of the Workbook contents. Inside there is much, much more to help you revise. For example:

- lots of samples of students' own work at different levels
- help with spelling, punctuation and grammar
- advice and tasks on writing about context
- a full answer key so you can check your answers
- a full-length practice exam task with guidance on what to focus on.

PART TWO: PLOT AND ACTION

Chapter 1: The Science of Deduction

QUICK TEST

❶ Look at these statements about Chapter 1. For each one decide whether it is **TRUE [T]**, **FALSE [F]**, or whether there is **Not Enough Evidence [NEE]** to decide:

a) Holmes injects himself with morphine. [T] Ⓕ [NEE]

b) Watson does not like Holmes taking drugs. Ⓣ [F] [NEE]

c) Watson is still recovering from fighting in South Africa. [T] [F] (NEE)

d) Holmes wrote an account of his last case called A Study in Scarlet. [T] Ⓕ [NEE]

e) Holmes has been recently helping an Italian detective. [T] Ⓕ [NEE]

f) Watson gives Holmes a watch as a test of his deduction skills. Ⓣ [F] [NEE]

g) The weather is warm and sunny outside. [T] Ⓕ [NEE]

h) Mrs Hudson has been spring cleaning. [T] [F] (NEE)

THINKING MORE DEEPLY

❷ Write **one** or **two sentences** in response to each of these questions:

a) What is Holmes's attitude towards being a detective?

He doesn't care about the notority he could gain through the newspaper. Instead, he view being a detective as a medium to use and express his 'peculiar powers' through, and finds pleasure in that. He believes a detective must be void of emotion and use only observation, deduction and knowledge to solve a case.

b) What do we learn about Watson's background?

A drunkard.

Watson was a doctor in the war. He has a careless brother and a father who had 'occasional short intervals of prosperity' a was 'a man of untidy habits'.

c) How does Holmes attempt to justify his use of cocaine to his worried friend, Watson?

He claims the 'transcendently stimulating' effects on his mind far outweigh the negative side effects on his health. He hates being bored more than the damage the cocaine causes.

EXAM PREPARATION: WRITING ABOUT CHARACTER

Read the extract, from *'Yet upon that afternoon'* (p. 1) to *'a relish for conversation.'* (p. 2)

Question: What impression do you get of Watson's attitude towards Holmes in this conversation?

Think about:

- The words used to present Holmes's surprising and worrying behaviour
- Watson's different feelings about Holmes's methods of deduction

❸ Complete this table:

Point/detail	Evidence	Effect or explanation
1: *Watson hates seeing Holmes injecting himself with cocaine.*	*'from day to day I had become more irritable at the sight, and my conscience swelled nightly within me'*	*Conan Doyle shows that Watson worries about Holmes both in the day and 'nightly' revealing how much he cares for his friend.*
2: *Watson understands that he has a complex relationship with Holmes.*	'I speak not only as one comrade to another, but as a medical man to one for whose constitution he is to some extent answerable.'	Watson is shown as concerned and protective of Watson, yet as feels the need to highlight his experience as a doctor as justification, showing their complex relationship.
3: *Watson is reluctant to upset Holmes by questioning him, even if he does not always understand him.*	'But consider!' 'why would you...risk the loss of those great powers with which you have been endowed?'	Watson or is shown as not wanting to upset Holmes as he makes sure to try and compliment Holmes whilst questioning him. as well as by using polite language like 'consider'. He says he is 'diffident'

❹ Write up **point 1** into a **paragraph** below, in your own words. Remember to include what you infer from the evidence, or the writer's effects:

In chapter I, watson clearly disapproves of Holmes' use of cocaine claiming he 'had become more irritable at the sight' and that his 'conscience swelled nightly' proving watsons deep dislike of cocaine and that it greatly impacts him to see his friend use it.

❺ Now, choose **one** of your **other points** and write it out as another **paragraph** here:

Watson, although disapproving of Sherlock's drug use does not want to upset him. He tries to get Sherlock himself to 'consider!' it himself and tries to get him to see what he would lose. In this way, watson is giving his opinion whilst urging Sherlock himself to make a decision, rather than forcing him.

PROGRESS LOG [tick the correct box] Needs more work ☐ Getting there ☐ Under control ☑

Chapter 2: The Statement of the Case

QUICK TEST

❶ Complete this **gap-fill paragraph** about the chapter, with the **correct or suitable information:**

Miss Morstan is a ....young....... lady who clearly makes a strong impression on ..W.atson...........

She tells Holmes and Watson about her father who had come home from .India.. ten years ago

and then vanished, never to be seen again. Her mother is also dead and so she has lived a

........lonely.............. life. A further mystery lies in the fact that she is being sent a valuable

........pearl.............. every year on her father Birthday.... Miss Morstan decided to seek

help when she received a letter that morning stating that she will receive ...justice..............

if she attends a meeting later that day at the Lyceum Theatre. Watson and Holmes

........Keenly.......... agree to come to the meeting with her.

THINKING MORE DEEPLY

❷ Write **one** or **two sentences** in response to each of these questions:

a) In what circumstances did Captain Morstan disappear?

Although he had arrived in London safely, he had left the Hotel where he was meant to meet Mrs Morstan, the night before.

b) Why does Holmes call Miss Morstan 'a model client'?

She is organised and has all the evidence Sherlock needs ready with her. She is also well informed and is able to answer whatever Sherlock asks.

c) How does Chapter 2 help us understand that Britain was viewed as a powerful country all around the world at this time?

It talks about colonisation in India at the time and shows India was part of the British Empire. This shows that Britain had a large empire on the opposite side of the world showing it's power.

EXAM PREPARATION: WRITING ABOUT THEME

A01

Read Watson's final comments in this chapter in the last paragraph, from
'I sat in the window' to 'will-o'-the-wisps of the imagination.' (p. 16)

Question: How does Conan Doyle introduce the theme of romance between Watson and Miss Morstan?

Think about:

- The words that Conan Doyle uses to present Watson's feelings
- The contrast between Watson's and Holmes's feelings

❸ Complete this table:

Point/detail	Evidence	Effect or explanation
1: *Conan Doyle shows that Watson cannot concentrate on his book.*	*'my thoughts were far from the daring speculations of the writer'*	*Watson describes the book as 'daring', but even so he thinks more about Miss Morstan. The reader might infer that Watson's real life is actually more exciting than the book he is reading.*
2: *Conan Doyle suggests that Watson and Miss Morstan are compatible because of their ages.*	'Must be seven and twenty now – a sweet age, when youth has lost it self conciousness and has become spaced by experience'.	Watson justifies his attraction for Mrs Morstan by claiming she is at a good age and therefore more suitable for him: 'sober'.
3: *Watson realises his romantic feelings about Miss Morstan are very different from Holmes's feelings.*	'A client to me is a unit, a mere factor in a problem'.	In contrast to Watson's romantic take on Miss Morstan, sherlock is characteristicaly unemotional and sees her not as a person but as a 'factor' and a part of the mystery, which occupys his attention.

❹ Write up **point 1** into a **paragraph** below, in your own words. Remember to include what you infer from the evidence, or the writer's effects:

Conan Doyle is unable to concentrate on his book, because of Miss Morstan, his thoughts far 'from the daring speculations of the writer'. Despite the 'daring book', his present situation is more relevant and exciting to him and he finds Miss Morstan far more interesting than his book.

❺ Now, choose **one** of your **other points** and write it out as another **paragraph** here:

Watson, clearly taken by Miss Morstan, is suprised by Holmes' indifferent feelings towards her, regarding her only as a 'mere factor in a problem', an unemotional stance the Watson should peak second, as a helper in this case. In this way, the romance between Miss morstan and watson is seen as unproffesional and unsuitable for the circumstances.

PROGRESS LOG [tick the correct box]   Needs more work ☐   Getting there ☐   Under control ☐

Chapter 3: In Quest of a Solution

QUICK TEST ✓

1 Choose the correct answer to **finish the statement** and **tick the box**:

a) The pearls begin arriving in the post to Miss Morstan after:

the death of Major Sholto ✓

her twentieth birthday ☐

Christmas day ☐

b) Before they leave, Holmes:

puts a revolver in his pocket ✓

shuts all the windows ☐

plays the violin ☐

c) Miss Morstan found an important document:

in a locked box ☐

buried in the garden ☐

in Captain Morstan's pocket book ✓

d) The Lyceum Theatre is:

quiet and menacing ☐

crowded and busy ✓

closed ☐

e) As the coach travels through London, Holmes knows:

all the names of the coachmen ☐

all the names of the roads ✓

all the names of the shops ☐

f) The door is answered by:

a Hindoo servant ✓

an Irish priest ☐

an Australian farmer ☐

THINKING MORE DEEPLY ?

2 Write **one** or **two sentences** in response to each of these questions:

a) What different detecting techniques does Holmes demonstrate in this chapter?

Holmes uses deduction to connect the death of Major Sholto to the annual pearl Miss Morstan recieves revealing the possibility of a possible heir to Major Sholto who wants to compensate Miss Morstan.

b) In what ways does Watson show he is nervous when he is talking to Miss Morstan?

He rambles on about his time in Afghanistan and is described to have told stories that were 'slightly involved'. He tries to impress her with dramatic stories.

c) What is unusual about the house that they eventually arrive at?

None of the surrounding houses were inhabited. It is also the only house that has a light on. The door is opened and a Hindoo servant is waiting outside in national dress.

EXAM PREPARATION: WRITING ABOUT SETTING

Read the description of London, from *'It was a September evening'* to *'in the light of his pocket-lantern.'* (pp. 19–20)

Question: How does Conan Doyle present the city of London in this extract?

Think about:

- The atmosphere that Conan Doyle creates through his choice of words
- The details about people and setting that he chooses to focus on

❸ Complete this table:

Point/detail	Evidence	Effect or explanation
1: *The weather seems unusually dark.*	*'It was a September evening, and not yet seven o'clock, but the day had been a dreary one'*	*This is an example of pathetic fallacy, where the darkness reflects the 'fog' that the characters are in as they try to solve the mysteries.*
2: *The streetlights do not seem able to lift the darkness of the early evening.*	'Down the Strand the lamps were but misty spotches of diffused light.'	In this quote, the darkness overpowers the light of the lamp, as if darkness is all that lies ahead.
3: *The people of London are described as being ghostly and strange.*	'There was, to my mind, something eerie and ghostlike to the endless procession of faces which flitted across these narrow bars of light.'	In this quote, the people in the 'endless procession of faces' are nameless, without identity. This is alike the dead, and therefore ghosts.

❹ Write up **point 1** into a **paragraph** below, in your own words. Remember to include what you infer from the evidence, or the writer's effects:

The weather in London is described by Conan Doyle as particularly dark, the day a 'dreary one' even in an early september evening. This represents the lack of clarity the characters face as they head towards they their mysterious destination.

❺ Now, choose **one** of your **other points** and write it out as another **paragraph** here:

London is decribed as dark with even the lamps being just 'misty spotches of diffused light' useless in lifting the darkness of London. This implies that the night ahead will not go well and that any of actions to prevent it are futile, heightening suspence.

PROGRESS LOG [tick the correct box]   Needs more work ☐   Getting there ☐   Under control ☐

Chapter 4: The Story of the Bald-Headed Man

QUICK TEST

❶ Complete this **gap-fill paragraph** about the chapter, with the **correct or suitable information**:

In this chapter, Holmes, Watson and Miss Morstan meet ...*Thaddeus*... Sholto. His

appearance is quite strange and he seems to be very ....*nervous*.... . Sholto tells them

that he remembers the disappearance of .*Mr Morstan*.... but never dreamed that his

father was involved. However, his father, ...*Major*.... Sholto, later confessed

that he was with Morstan when he died and he had concealed the body. Thaddeus's father then died

before he could reveal where Captain Morstan's ....*treasure*.... was hidden. Thaddeus

and his brother ....*Bartholomew*.... decide to send Miss Morstan a pearl every year to

save her from poverty. Thaddeus then reveals that they have now found Captain Morstan's hidden

treasure and they will take Miss Morstan to claim it at *Pondicherry*.... Lodge.

THINKING MORE DEEPLY

❷ Write **one** or **two sentences** in response to each of these questions:

a) In what ways is Thaddeus Sholto an unusual character?

He is very enthusiastic and a vivid storyteller but also collects artifacts and describes himself as 'a patron of the arts' and is told by watson to be a 'confirmed hypochondriac.

b) What do we learn about 'The sign of the four' in this chapter?

That Major sholto kept a torn piece of paper with 'the sign of the four' on it although he never told his family about it.

c) What kind of relationship does Thaddeus appear to have with his brother Bartholomew?

They seem to be close, but are also very different, which causes them to argue, with him disagreeing with his brother's materialistic attitudes.

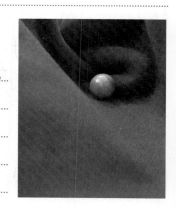

EXAM PREPARATION: WRITING ABOUT STRUCTURE

Read Major Sholto's description of his reaction to the death of Captain Morstan, from *'I was still pondering over the matter'* to *'but the man was gone.'* (p. 29)

Question: How does Conan Doyle structure this extract to engage the reader?

Think about:

- What information Conan Doyle reveals and when he does that
- How Conan Doyle selects images to interest the reader

❸ Complete this table:

Point/detail	Evidence	Effect or explanation
1: Conan Doyle creates a mystery around the location of Captain Morstan's body.	Major Sholto takes the advice of his servant and deliberately conceals the dead body, using the euphemism 'put him away'.	This is a callous act by Major Sholto which ensures that Miss Morstan will never be able to find her father's body and deepens the mystery around the treasure.
2: Major Sholto himself does not reveal the location of the treasure as he dies mid-sentence.	'The treasure is hidden in –' 'His pulse had ceased to beat'.	Major Sholto's explanation is disrupted and is never finished, leaving the location of the treasure unknown, to the sholtos in the past but sherlock now.
3: A terrifying and unidentified face appears at the window just as Major Sholto is about to explain where the treasure is.	'A face was looking in at us out of the darkness'	A face is seen at the window looking 'out of the darkness'. This scares Major sholto, so he is unable to explain the location of the treasure.

❹ Write up **point 1** into a **paragraph** below, in your own words. Remember to include what you infer from the evidence, or the writer's effects:

Conan Doyle has makes the location of Captain Morstan's body mysterious claiming a servant took it and 'put him away', leaving no further revelation on the location by Thaddeus, as may've been hoped by Miss Morstan. This goes on to build emphasis on finding the treasure, as it may reveal the location.

❺ Now, choose **one** of your **other points** and write it out as another **paragraph** here:

The appearance of the face at the window just before Major Sholto revealed where the treasure was, engages the reader, with it's sudden change in pace one increasing the mystery and revealing to the reader that the mystery is much darker, and more complicated than it seemed. 'looking out of the darkness'

PROGRESS LOG [tick the correct box]   Needs more work ☐   Getting there ☐   Under control ☐

Chapter 5: The Tragedy of Pondicherry Lodge

QUICK TEST

❶ From the list of names, **identify** the **character** or **characters** being referred to:

Dr Watson	*Miss Morstan*	*Thaddeus Sholto*
Sherlock Holmes	*Bartholomew Sholto*	*McMurdo*

a) 'I don't think <u>you</u> can have forgotten <u>me</u>. Don't <u>you</u> remember the amateur who fought three rounds with <u>you</u>' (p. 35) .... and ....

b) 'Does <u>he</u> always guard the premises in this way?' (p. 36) ....

c) 'So <u>we</u> stood hand in hand, like two children' (p. 37) .... and
....

d) '"There is something devilish in this, Watson," said <u>he</u>, more moved than I had ever before seen <u>him</u>.' (p. 39) ....

e) '<u>He</u> was stiff and cold and had clearly been dead many hours.' (p. 40) ....

f) 'This is all an insoluble mystery to <u>me</u>.' (p. 41) ....

g) 'Oh, dear! oh, dear! <u>I</u> know that <u>I</u> shall go mad!' (p. 41) ....

THINKING MORE DEEPLY

❷ Write **one** or **two sentences** in response to each of these questions:

a) In what ways is Watson's relationship with Miss Morstan developing?

....

....

....

....

b) How does Holmes's reaction to the death of Bartholomew Sholto differ from Thaddeus's?

....

....

....

....

c) How would you describe the appearance and atmosphere of Pondicherry Lodge?

....

....

....

....

EXAM PREPARATION: WRITING ABOUT LANGUAGE

Read the description of Bartholomew's dead body, from '*By the table*' to '*In God's name, what does it all mean?*' (p. 40)

Question: How does Conan Doyle use language to convey a sense of horror in this extract?

Think about:

- The words and phrases that have a particular effect on the reader
- The use of strange or shocking imagery

❸ Complete this table:

Point/detail	Evidence	Effect or explanation
1: Conan Doyle describes the dead body as appearing in an unnatural manner.	'the master of the house was seated all in a heap, with his head sunk upon his left shoulder'	The phrase 'master of the house' suggests power and control and contrasts greatly with the description 'all in a heap' which would shock the reader.
2: Conan Doyle gives disturbing and contradictory detail.		
3: The weapon used to kill Bartholomew is unusual in its appearance.		

❹ Write up **point 1** into a **paragraph** below, in your own words. Remember to include what you infer from the evidence, or the writer's effects:

....

....

....

....

....

❺ Now, choose **one** of your **other points** and write it out as another **paragraph** here:

....

....

....

....

....

PROGRESS LOG [tick the correct box]   Needs more work ☐   Getting there ☐   Under control ☐

Chapter 6: Sherlock Holmes Gives a Demonstration

QUICK TEST ✓

❶ Which of these statements about Chapter 6 are **TRUE**, and which are **FALSE**?
Write **'T'** or **'F'** in the boxes:

a) Holmes says the case is simple. ☐

b) The round prints are made with a walking stick. ☐

c) The intruder came in through a hole in the roof. ☐

d) The intruder has accidentally trodden in some paint. ☐

e) Athelney Jones remembers Holmes from the Bishopgate jewel case. ☐

f) Miss Morstan lives with her sister. ☐

g) Holmes requests that Watson fetches a dog called Toby to help them. ☐

THINKING MORE DEEPLY ?

❷ Write **one** or **two sentences** in response to each of these questions:

a) Why is the reference to the 'wooden-legged man' significant?

....

....

....

....

b) What more does the reader learn about the death of Bartholomew Sholto?

....

....

....

....

c) What impression is given of Athelney Jones here?

....

....

....

....

....

| EXAM PREPARATION: WRITING ABOUT CHARACTER | |

Read the description of Holmes, from '"*Now, Watson,*" *said Holmes, rubbing his hands*' to '"*It is absolutely impossible,*" *I answered.*' (pp. 43–4)

Question: What do we learn about Holmes's approach to the investigation in this extract?

Think about:

- The words and phrases that Holmes uses
- The way that Conan Doyle describes Holmes's behaviour

❸ Complete this table:

Point/detail	Evidence	Effect or explanation
1: *Holmes appears to be excited about solving the case.*	'*rubbing his hands*'	*The fact that Holmes is 'rubbing his hands' suggests that he is ready to work and is looking forward to it.*
2: *Holmes has a detached manner, even though the facts of the case are horrific and shocking.*		
3: *Holmes enjoys involving Watson in his investigation.*		

❹ Write up **point 1** into a **paragraph** below in your own words. Remember to include what you infer from the evidence, or the writer's effects:

....

....

....

....

....

❺ Now, choose **one** of your **other points** and write it out as another **paragraph** here:

....

....

....

....

....

| PROGRESS LOG [tick the correct box] | Needs more work ☐ | Getting there ☐ | Under control ☐ |

Chapter 7: The Episode of the Barrel

QUICK TEST ✔

❶ Choose the correct answer to **finish the statement** and **tick the box**:

a) Watson is reluctant to express his love for Miss Morstan because:

she could soon be very rich ☐

he is married already ☐

Holmes advised him not to ☐

b) Watson compares the mystery of the treasure to:

a board game ☐

a labyrinth ☐

a football match ☐

c) Holmes has sent Watson to Mr Sherman to borrow a:

gun ☐

boat ☐

dog ☐

d) Holmes finds a box full of:

poisoned darts ☐

bullets ☐

pencil leads ☐

e) Toby the dog wrongly leads them to a:

churchyard ☐

timber-yard ☐

library ☐

THINKING MORE DEEPLY ?

❷ Write **one** or **two sentences** in response to each of these questions:

a) What kind of home does Miss Morstan live in?

....

....

....

....

b) What do we learn about Jonathan Small in this chapter?

....

....

....

....

c) How can we tell that Holmes is confident about solving the case?

....

....

....

....

EXAM PREPARATION: WRITING ABOUT STYLE

Read the description of Watson collecting Toby the dog, from '*Pinchin Lane was a row of shabby two-storied brick houses*' to '*as our voices disturbed their slumbers.*' (pp. 55–6)

Question: How does Conan Doyle bring humour to this part of the novella?

Think about:

- The language used to describe Watson's unusual situation
- The way that Mr Sherman speaks to Watson

❸ Complete this table:

Point/detail	Evidence	Effect or explanation
1: *Watson finds himself being treated in a way that he is not used to at all.*	*Mr Sherman is very rude to Watson.*	*It is funny for the reader to hear Watson described as 'drunken' as he always behaves sensibly. He is also smartly dressed and unlike a 'vagabone' which creates humour.*
2: *Mr Sherman uses some non-standard English which contrasts with Watson's more 'educated' speech.*		
3: *Mr Sherman keeps a strange collection of animals in his house.*		

❹ Write up **point 1** into a **paragraph** below, in your own words. Remember to include what you infer from the evidence, or the writer's effects:

....

....

....

....

❺ Now, choose **one** of your **other points** and write it out as another **paragraph** here:

....

....

....

....

....

PROGRESS LOG [tick the correct box]   Needs more work 🔲   Getting there 🔲   Under control 🔲

Chapter 8: The Baker Street Irregulars

QUICK TEST ✓

❶ Complete this **gap-fill paragraph** about the chapter, with the **correct** or **suitable information**:

Holmes and Watson follow .... to the river Thames where

Holmes realises the suspects have escaped in a boat. Holmes speaks to the .... of

Mordecai Smith who confirms that Mordecai has taken a boat out with a man with a wooden leg.

In the morning the .... report the death of Bartholomew Sholto and that

Athelney Jones has arrested all the members of the household at .... Holmes

pays the .... to search for Mordecai's boat, called the ....

Holmes reveals that he has deduced that Small's .... must have been a native of

the Andaman Islands. Finally, Watson falls asleep as Holmes plays his ....

THINKING MORE DEEPLY ?

❷ Write **one** or **two sentences** in response to each of these questions:

a) Why does Toby take Holmes and Watson to the wrong place?

....

....

....

....

b) How does Holmes manage to get the information he needs from Mrs Smith?

....

....

....

....

c) How do Holmes's and Watson's attitudes to lack of sleep differ from each other?

....

....

....

....

....

EXAM PREPARATION: WRITING ABOUT CHARACTER

Read the description of Jonathan Small's accomplice, from *'That other man again!'* (p. 74) to *'not to have employed him.'* (p. 75)

Question: How does Conan Doyle present Small's accomplice here?

Think about:

- The words and phrases used to describe the accomplice's appearance
- The details of the accomplice's behaviour

❸ Complete this table:

Point/detail	Evidence	Effect or explanation
1: *Conan Doyle uses a range of details that imply the accomplice is barely human.*	*The man is referred to as a 'savage' and is linked to 'massacres' and cannibal feasts.*	*It was not unusual in Conan Doyle's time for the natives of overseas colonies that the British had settled in to be seen as inferior to British or Western people.*
2: *Conan Doyle describes unusual physical characteristics of the accomplice.*		
3: *Holmes quotes from a scientific journal about foreign tribes which explains that natives of the Andaman Islands are violent.*		

❹ Write up **point 1** into a **paragraph** below, in your own words. Remember to include what you infer from the evidence, or the writer's effects:

....

....

....

....

....

❺ Now, choose **one** of your **other points** and write it out as another **paragraph** here:

....

....

....

....

....

....

PROGRESS LOG [tick the correct box]   Needs more work 🔲   Getting there 🔲   Under control 🔲

Chapter 9: A Break in the Chain

QUICK TEST ✓

❶ Choose the correct answer to **finish the statement** and **tick the box**:

a) Sherlock Holmes is anxious because no one can find:

Holmes's violin ☐

the key to the treasure box ☐

Mordecai Smith's boat ☐

b) Watson visits:

Miss Morstan ☐

Thaddeus Sholto ☐

Jonathan Small ☐

c) Holmes decides to go to the riverside wearing:

sailor's clothes ☐

a formal suit ☐

a deerstalker hat ☐

d) Watson receives a house call from:

Athelney Jones ☐

Mr Sherman ☐

Tonga ☐

e) Holmes makes a plan to find:

the treasure ☐

Toby the dog ☐

Miss Morstan ☐

f) Holmes says that you should not trust:

the police ☐

doctors ☐

women ☐

THINKING MORE DEEPLY ❓

❷ Write **one** or **two sentences** in response to each of these questions:

a) What is Miss Morstan's attitude towards the treasure?

....

....

....

....

b) Why does Watson feel concerned about Holmes's ability to solve the case?

....

....

....

....

c) Why does Holmes dress in disguise?

....

....

....

....

EXAM PREPARATION: WRITING ABOUT CHARACTER **A01**

Read the conversation between Holmes and Athelney Jones, from '*Never mind.*' to '*I don't see how I can refuse you an interview with him.*' (pp. 86–7)

Question: How does Conan Doyle convey Holmes's ability to control this stage of the investigation?

Think about:

- The way that Conan Doyle describes Holmes and Athelney Jones speaking to each other
- Holmes's decisions about how to continue the search

❸ Complete this table:

Point/detail	Evidence	Effect or explanation
1: *Conan Doyle shows that it is essential to Holmes that he is completely in charge of events.*	*Holmes insists that Athelney Jones follows his instructions exactly: 'you must put yourself under my orders'*	*The modal verb 'must' conveys Holmes's determination and control and the phrase 'under my orders' implies that Holmes is fully in charge.*
2: *Athelney Jones not only takes Holmes's order, he also asks for further requests.*		
3: *Conan Doyle shows that Holmes is even able to make unusual requests.*		

❹ Write up **point 1** into a **paragraph** below, in your own words. Remember to include what you infer from the evidence, or the writer's effects:

....

....

....

❺ Now, choose **one** of your **other points** and write it out as another **paragraph** here:

....

....

....

....

....

PROGRESS LOG [tick the correct box]   Needs more work ☐   Getting there ☐   Under control ☐

Chapter 10: The End of the Islander

QUICK TEST ✔

❶ Which of these statements about Chapter 10 are **TRUE**, and which are **FALSE**?

Write 'T' or 'F' in the boxes:

a) Holmes tells Watson to take a pistol when they go out. ☐

b) Jonathan Small had kept a continual watch over Pondicherry Lodge. ☐

c) Jonathan Small stole the boat from Mordecai Smith. ☐

d) Holmes visited fifteen boat yards before he found the one with the Aurora. ☐

e) The Aurora can be identified by its red light. ☐

f) Small's accomplice is killed by falling in the water. ☐

g) There is no key to the treasure box. ☐

THINKING MORE DEEPLY ❓

❷ Write **one** or **two sentences** in response to each of these questions:

a) Why was Holmes unable to find Mordecai Smith's boat (the Aurora)?

....

....

....

b) How is Small's accomplice described?

....

....

....

c) How do Holmes and Watson react to the events that have taken place on the river?

....

....

....

....

....

....

....

....

EXAM PREPARATION: WRITING ABOUT STYLE

Read the description of the chase along the river, from '"*She is very fast,*" *he said*' to '*still we followed close upon her track.*' (pp. 94–5)

Question: How does Conan Doyle convey the excitement of the chase?

Think about:

- The verbs and adjectives Conan Doyle uses
- The details that are presented to the reader

❸ Complete this table:

Point/detail	Evidence	Effect or explanation
1: *Conan Doyle conveys excitement through the reckless way that Holmes behaves.*	*Holmes encourages the crew to sail the boat fast: 'If we burn the boat we must have them!'*	*Holmes risks setting fire to the boat, but the use of the verb 'must' conveys his desperation.*
2: *Watson is impressed by the immense power of the boat engines.*		
3: *The Aurora is described as speeding ahead of Holmes's boat as if it might get away from them at any time.*		

❹ Write up **point 1** into a **paragraph** below, in your own words. Remember to include what you infer from the evidence, or the writer's effects:

....

....

....

....

....

❺ Now, choose **one** of your **other points** and write it out as another **paragraph** here:

....

....

....

....

....

....

PROGRESS LOG [tick the correct box]   Needs more work ☐   Getting there ☐   Under control ☐

Chapter 11: The Great Agra Treasure

❶ Complete this **gap-fill paragraph** about the chapter, with the **correct** or **suitable information**:

At the start of the chapter we see that .... has been arrested

and he now tells the story of the treasure. Holmes offers him a .... and a

drink from his flask. Small explains that he did not plan to kill ....

because he thought the room would be empty when he broke into ....,

and he was angry with .... for firing the poisoned dart. Small says the

treasure is nothing but a .... to anyone who comes across it. Small says

the key to the treasure box is now in .... When Watson breaks into the

box at Miss Morstan's house, they discover it is............................... .

THINKING MORE DEEPLY

❷ Write **one** or **two sentences** in response to each of these questions:

a) What do we learn about Jonathan Small's attitude towards Tonga, his accomplice?

....

....

....

....

b) How can we tell that Athelney Jones has taken charge of the situation once more?

....

....

....

....

....

c) Why is Watson pleased that the treasure box is empty?

....

....

....

....

....

EXAM PREPARATION: WRITING ABOUT CHARACTER

Read the description of Miss Morstan, from '*She was seated by the open window*' to '*she glanced at me curiously*.' (pp. 102–3)

Question: How does Conan Doyle present Miss Morstan at this stage of the novella?

Think about:

- Miss Morstan's behaviour
- The ways that Victorian women were expected to behave

❸ Complete this table:

Point/detail	Evidence	Effect or explanation
1: *Conan Doyle has presented Miss Morstan as a lonely figure earlier in the novella and this is suggested here too.*	*She is pictured sitting alone in the window of her home, with an air of 'absorbing melancholy'*	*The word 'absorbing' conveys the sense that Miss Morstan can be taken over by her sadness or 'melancholy' which is beyond her control.*
2: *Conan Doyle describes Miss Morstan as a particularly gentle and virtuous young woman.*		
3: *She seems to be a woman who is associated with the home and a quiet, unadventurous life.*		

❹ Write up **point 1** into a **paragraph** below, in your own words. Remember to include what you infer from the evidence, or the writer's effects:

....

....

....

....

....

❺ Now, choose **one** of your **other points** and write it out as another **paragraph** here:

....

....

....

....

....

....

| **PROGRESS LOG** [tick the correct box] | Needs more work ☐ | Getting there ☐ | Under control ☐ |

Chapter 12: The Strange Story of Jonathan Small

QUICK TEST ✔

❶ **Number** these events in Jonathan Small's life so that they are in the **correct sequence**. Use **1** for the first event and **8** for the final event:

a) Small makes a deal with Major Sholto and Captain Morstan to share the treasure. ☐

b) After losing his leg to a crocodile, he finds a job as an overseer on a plantation. ☐

c) Small throws the treasure into the river Thames. ☐

d) Jonathan Small meets three men in Agra who share the secret of the treasure. ☐

e) Small joins the British army in India when he is eighteen to escape trouble at home. ☐

f) Small tracks down Major Sholto in London, who has stolen the treasure for himself. ☐

g) Jonathan Small and Tonga steal the treasure from Bartholomew Sholto's laboratory. ☐

h) Small is arrested and imprisoned by the British at the Andaman Islands. ☐

THINKING MORE DEEPLY ❓

❷ Write **one** or **two sentences** in response to each of these questions:

a) Why does Jonathan Small throw the Agra treasure into the river?

....

....

....

....

b) What impression do we get of Major Sholto in this chapter?

....

....

....

....

c) Why does Homes claim he will 'never marry' (p. 132)?

....

....

....

....

....

EXAM PREPARATION: WRITING ABOUT TENSION

Read Small's account of the attack at the palace of Agra, from *'The third night of my watch was dark and dirty'* to *'what it was that they wanted from me.'* (pp. 113–14)

Question: How does Conan Doyle create tension and excitement in this extract?

Think about:

- How Conan Doyle conveys the sudden violence
- The threats that Jonathan Small faces

❸ Complete this table:

Point/detail	Evidence	Effect or explanation
1: Conan Doyle begins the passage at a quiet time of the night when little appears to be happening.	'It was dreary work'	This builds tension from a low point because the reader is surprised when Small is attacked by two Sikh men, one of whom holds a 'great knife' to his throat.
2: Conan Doyle describes the moments when Small has a knife at his throat in great detail.		
3: Conan Doyle increases the tension when the attacker unexpectedly tells Small that the fort is not actually under attack.		

❹ Write up **point 1** into a **paragraph** below, in your own words. Remember to include what you infer from the evidence, or the writer's effects:

....

....

....

....

❺ Now, choose **one** of your **other points** and write it out as another **paragraph** here:

....

....

....

....

....

....

PROGRESS LOG [tick the correct box]   Needs more work ☐   Getting there ☐   Under control ☐

Practice task

❶ First, **read** this **exam-style** task:

Read from *'This is all very well'* to *'the secret room in which the treasure was found.'* (pp. 44–5)

Question: How does Conan Doyle present the relationship between Holmes and Watson in this extract?

❷ Begin by circling the **key words** in the **question** above.

❸ Now, complete this table, noting down **3–4 key points** with **evidence** and the **effect** created:

Point	Evidence/quotation	Effect or explanation

❹ **Draft your response.** Use the space below for your first paragraph(s) and then continue onto a sheet of paper:

Start: *In this extract, Conan Doyle presents Watson as having mixed feelings about*

Holmes's ideas … ....

....

....

....

....

....

....

....

....

....

PROGRESS LOG [tick the correct box]   Needs more work ☐   Getting there ☐   Under control ☐

PART THREE: CHARACTERS

Who's who?

Look at these drawings and complete the **name** or **brief description** of each of the characters shown:

a) Mrs Forrester

Who: ....

....

....

b) Name: ....

....

Captain Morstan's
daughter

c) Mrs Hudson

Who: ....

....

....

d) Name: ....

....

Holmes's closest
friend

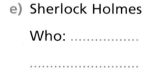

e) Sherlock Holmes

Who: ....

....

....

f) Name: ....

....

Police detective

g) Name: ....

....

Son of Major Sholto

h) Name: ....

....

Tracker dog

i) Jonathan Small

Who: ....

....

....

j) Mr Sherman

Who: ....

....

....

k) Name: ....

....

Street children

l) Tonga

Who: ....

....

....

PROGRESS LOG [tick the correct box]   Needs more work ☐   Getting there ☐   Under control ☐

Sherlock Holmes

❶ Look at these statements about Sherlock Holmes. For each one, decide whether it is **True [T]** or **False [F]**. Write **'T'** or **'F'** in the boxes:

a) Holmes hates not having any work to do. ☐

b) Holmes has a wife and children. ☐

c) Holmes won a fight as an amateur boxer. ☐

d) Holmes plays the trumpet. ☐

e) Holmes gets easily lost in London. ☐

f) Holmes is friends with Mrs Forrester. ☐

❷ Each of the **character traits** or **qualities** below could be applied to Sherlock Holmes. Working from memory, **add a point in the novella** when you think each trait is shown. Then find at least one quotation to support each idea:

Quality	Moment(s) in novella	Quotation
a) restless		
b) rational		
c) unpredictable		
d) confident		
e) highly intelligent		

❸ Using your **own judgement**, put a mark along this line to show **Conan Doyle's overall presentation** of Sherlock Holmes:

Totally unsympathetic   A little sympathetic   Quite sympathetic   Very sympathetic

❶   ❷   ❸   ❹

PROGRESS LOG [tick the correct box]   Needs more work ☐   Getting there ☐   Under control ☐

Dr Watson

❶ Look at this bank of **adjectives** describing Dr Watson. **Circle** the ones you think best **describe** him:

questioning	considerate	furious	lazy
thoughtful	romantic	loyal	violent
sensitive	cruel	humble	artistic

❷ Now add a **page reference** from your copy of the novella next to each circle, showing where **evidence** can be found to **support** the **adjective**.

❸ Complete this **gap-fill** paragraph about Watson, adding the **correct** or **suitable information**:

Dr Watson ……………………………………. the story, which means we see all the action from his

point of view. Watson has a background in the army as a ……………………………….., but this

was where he sustained an injury which still causes him ……………………………….. . Watson is

Holmes's ……………………………….. and is happy to listen as Holmes thinks through his

ideas. Holmes falls in love with …………………………….. when he first meets her but he is aware

that he has very little ……………………………………. which means he might not potentially be a

good husband for her. Watson is a …………………………….. character who takes on all the dangers

that the investigation brings his way.

❹ Using your own **judgement**, put a mark along this line to show **Conan Doyle's overall presentation** of Dr Watson:

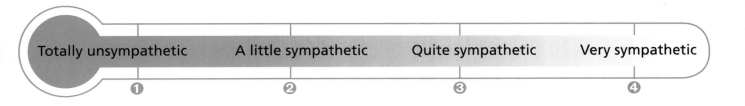

Totally unsympathetic   A little sympathetic   Quite sympathetic   Very sympathetic

❶   ❷   ❸   ❹

PROGRESS LOG [tick the correct box]   Needs more work ☐   Getting there ☐   Under control ☐

Miss Morstan

❶ Look at these statements about Miss Morstan. For each one, decide whether it is **True [T]**, **False [F]** or whether there is **Not Enough Evidence [NEE]** to decide:

a) Miss Morstan asks for Holmes's help after a robbery at her house.   [T] [F] [NEE]

b) Miss Morstan's parents are both dead.   [T] [F] [NEE]

c) Dr Watson falls in love with Miss Morstan.   [T] [F] [NEE]

d) Miss Morstan is excited about the treasure.   [T] [F] [NEE]

e) Miss Morstan loves to go shopping.   [T] [F] [NEE]

f) Holmes says that Miss Morstan is an ideal client.   [T] [F] [NEE]

g) Miss Morstan is often angry and bad-tempered.   [T] [F] [NEE]

❷ Complete these **statements** about Miss Morstan:

a) *We first meet Miss Morstan when she visits …*

b) *Holmes has been recommended to her by …*

c) *Every year on her birthday Miss Morstan has received …*

d) *Miss Morstan is fearful about her father because …*

e) *When Watson tells her he was nearly shot with a poisoned dart, Miss Morstan …*

❸ Write a short **paragraph** explaining the typical Victorian attitudes to women that Conan Doyle represents through Miss Morstan:

PROGRESS LOG [tick the correct box]   Needs more work ☐   Getting there ☐   Under control ☐

Thaddeus Sholto

❶ Look at this bank of **adjectives** describing Thaddeus Sholto. **Circle** the ones you think best **describe** him:

fair	*artistic*	*wronged*	*spiteful*	*honest*
uneducated	*responsible*		*athletic*	*violent*
comic	*loyal*	*grateful*	*kind*	*eccentric*

❷ Now add a **page reference** from your copy of the novella next to each circle, showing where evidence can be found to support the adjective.

❸ Complete this **gap-fill paragraph** about Thaddeus, adding the **correct or suitable information**:

Thaddeus Sholto is the son of ....and the twin brother of

.... He lives in a house that is decorated with ....

items. Thaddeus sees himself as part of an .... movement in London. He

believes that his father was .... to keep the treasure from ....

and he is the one who decided to send her a ....every year. Although

.... puts him under arrest, he is ....of any wrong-

doing and does everything he can to help Holmes and Watson find the ....

❹ 'Thaddeus Sholto lives an unusual lifestyle but in many ways he is a typical Victorian gentleman.'

To what extent do you agree with this statement? Try to give **two** or **three points** in your answer:

....

....

....

....

....

....

....

....

PROGRESS LOG [tick the correct box]   Needs more work ☐   Getting there ☐   Under control ☐

Jonathan Small

❶ Look at these statements about Jonathan Small. For each one, decide whether it is **True [T]**, **False [F]** or whether there is **Not Enough Evidence [NEE]** to decide:

a) Small is one of 'the four'. [T] [F] [NEE]

b) Small lost his leg after being shot. [T] [F] [NEE]

c) Small is imprisoned in a British colony in India. [T] [F] [NEE]

d) Small makes an agreement with Bartholomew Sholto to hide the treasure. [T] [F] [NEE]

e) Small leaves the note with 'The sign of the four' on Major Sholto's dead body. [T] [F] [NEE]

f) Small admires Sherlock Holmes. [T] [F] [NEE]

g) Small killed Bartholomew Sholto. [T] [F] [NEE]

❷ Each of the **character traits** or **qualities** below could be applied to Jonathan Small. Working from memory, **add a point in the novella** when you think each trait is shown. Then find at least one **quotation** to support each idea:

Quality	Moment(s) in novella	Quotation
a) ironic		
b) determined		
c) passionate		
d) violent		

❸ Using your own **judgement**, put a mark along this line to show **Conan Doyle's overall presentation** of Jonathan Small:

Totally unsympathetic	A little sympathetic	Quite sympathetic	Very sympathetic
❶	❷	❸	❹

PROGRESS LOG [tick the correct box] Needs more work ☐ Getting there ☐ Under control ☐

Athelney Jones

❶ Complete these **statements** about Athelney Jones:

a) *Athelney Jones first appears in the novella after …*

....

b) *Athelney Jones is a detective who is based at …*

....

c) *After the death of Bartholomew Sholto, Athelney Jones arrests …*

....

d) *Atheleny Jones criticises Holmes's methods, saying that he is …*

....

e) *Athelney Jones helps in the river chase by agreeing to …*

....

f) *Although they are professional rivals, Jones and Holmes are generally …*

....

❷ Look at this **quotation** from Athelney Jones. Add **annotations** to it by selecting suitable **adjectives** from the word bank below. Then for each one, **explain** how Conan Doyle's words help to convey Jones's character and his attitude towards Sherlock Holmes in the extract:

sarcastic =
Jones refer to → It's Mr. Sherlock Holmes, the theorist. Remember you!
Holmes in the   I'll never forget how you lectured us all on causes and
third person   inferences and effects in the Bishopgate jewel case.
even though   It's true you set us on the right track: but you'll own now
he is standing   that it was more by good luck than good guidance. (p. 48)
in front of him

sarcastic	impolite	gentle	furious
helpful	critical	calm	

PROGRESS LOG [tick the correct box]   Needs more work ☐   Getting there ☐   Under control ☐

Minor characters

❶ Write the **name** from the list next to the **correct description** below:

Mrs Forrester	*Lal Rao*	*Mrs Hudson*
Mr Sherman	*McMurdo*	*Wiggins*

a) A 'prize-fighter' (boxer) who works for Bartholomew Sholto ....

b) A butler for Thaddeus Sholto ....

c) Miss Morstan's friend and employer ....

d) Sherlock Holmes's housekeeper and landlady ....

e) The leader of the 'Baker Street Irregulars' ....

f) An animal keeper who owns Toby the tracker dog ....

❷ Briefly **explain** how these minor characters are **connected** to Jonathan Small:

a) Tonga

....

b) Bartholomew Sholto

....

c) Mordecai Smith

....

d) Abdullah Khan

....

....

e) Mr Abelwhite

....

....

f) Major Sholto

....

....

....

PROGRESS LOG [tick the correct box]   Needs more work ☐   Getting there ☐   Under control ☐

Practice task

❶ First, **read** this **exam-style** task:

Read from '*You are deceiving us, Small*' to '*when he first learned that the injured convict was upon his track.*' (pp. 107–8)

Question: How does Conan Doyle present Jonathan Small as both a victim and a villain in this extract and in the novella as a whole?

❷ Begin by circling the **key words** in the **question** above.

❸ Now complete this table, noting down **3–4 key points** with **evidence** and the **effect** created:

Point	Evidence/quotation	Effect or explanation

❹ **Draft your response.** Use the space below for your first paragraph(s) and then continue onto a sheet of paper:

Start: *In this extract, Conan Doyle presents Small as a character who is a victim of ...*

PROGRESS LOG [tick the correct box] Needs more work ☐ Getting there ☐ Under control ☐

PART FOUR: Themes, Contexts and Settings

Themes

❶ Complete this **gap-fill** paragraph about the **theme** of **friendship and loyalty**, adding the **correct or suitable information**:

'The Sign of the Four' presents a number of friendships and alliances, but the central relationship

is between Holmes and ...., the narrator of the novella. They are very

different ....: Holmes is .... whereas

Watson is more emotional in his responses. Watson will take great .... for

Holmes, and constantly expresses .... at Holmes's abilities. Holmes is

.... towards Watson, for example lulling him to sleep by playing the violin.

A friendship is destroyed with the betrayal of Major Sholto by .... However,

Jonathan Small also shows himself to be a loyal friend to the ...., and puts

himself in great danger to fulfil their plans, ending in his arrest.

❷ These comments by different characters suggest a particular **theme** in the novella. Choose the best **abstract noun** from the box below to identify the theme in each one:

a) 'I caught one glimpse of his venomous, menacing eyes amid the white swirl of the waters.' **(p. 97)**

Theme: ....

b) 'Sherlock Holmes and I looked blankly at each other, and then burst simultaneously into an uncontrollable fit of laughter.' **(p. 65)**

Theme: ....

c) 'One month India lay as still and peaceful, to all appearance, as Surrey or Kent; the next there were two hundred thousand black devils let loose ...' **(p. 110)**

Theme: ....

d) 'The richest and glossiest of curtains and tapestries draped the walls ...' **(p. 24)**

Theme: ....

e) 'I cared nothing for the law,– nothing for the gallows. To escape, to track down Sholto, to have my hand upon his throat,– that was my one thought.' **(p. 127)**

Theme: ....

revenge	*forgiveness*	*wealth*	*colonialism*
justice	*friendship*	*otherness*	*poverty*

❸ Write **two** or **three sentences** to show how quotations a) and b) in Question 2 reveal their themes. Include a **comment** on the **writer's effects**:

a) *Conan Doyle's description of the drowning Tonga …* ....

....

....

b) *Conan Doyle develops our understanding of the friendship between Holmes and Watson by …*

....

....

....

THINKING MORE DEEPLY ❓

❹ **Complete** each **statement** about the **theme** of **crime**:

a) *Captain Morstan's crime of helping to steal the Agra treasure was committed out of …*

....

....

b) *Jonathan Small falls into a life of crime because …* ....

....

....

c) *Sherlock Holmes's approach to solving crime includes …* ....

....

....

d) *Major Sholto's crime of disposing of Captain Morstan's body has the effect of…* ....

....

....

....

PROGRESS LOG [tick the correct box]   Needs more work ☐   Getting there ☐   Under control ☐

⑤ Write **one** or **two sentences** in response to each of these questions about the **themes of the novella**. Include a comment on the **writer's effects**:

a) How does the story of Tonga present to the reader the negative effects of colonialism?

....

....

....

b) How do Bartholomew and Thaddeus Sholto present the theme of family ties and tensions?

....

....

....

c) In what ways is Miss Morstan's life restricted by being a single woman in Victorian society?

....

....

....

⑥ Write **one** or **two sentences** to show how Conan Doyle uses language in these quotations to explore the **theme** of **duality**:

a) Holmes: *'... the most winning woman I ever knew was hanged for poisoning three little children for their insurance-money.'* (p. 15)

....

....

....

b) Thaddeus Sholto: *'Over this chaplet my Brother Bartholomew and I had some little discussion. The pearls were evidently of great value, and he was averse to part with them, for, between friends, my brother was himself a little inclined to my father's fault.'* (p. 31)

....

....

....

c) Holmes: *'Viewing the matter as an abstract problem, I had forgotten how personal and painful a thing it might be to you.'* (p. 8)

....

....

....

PROGRESS LOG [tick the correct box]   Needs more work ☐   Getting there ☐   Under control ☐

EXAM PREPARATION: WRITING ABOUT THE THEME OF FRIENDSHIP

Read the section of Chapter 1 from *'This is unworthy of you, Holmes'* to *'May I ask if whether you have any professional inquiry on foot at present?'* (pp. 8–9)

Question: How does Conan Doyle present the friendship between Holmes and Watson in this passage?

Think about:

- How Watson reacts to Holmes's apparent insensitivity
- How Holmes tries to calm Watson

❼ Complete this table:

Point/detail	Evidence	Effect or explanation
1: *Watson is horrified at the thought that Holmes has tried to deceive him.*	*'you now pretend to deduce this knowledge in some fanciful way'*	*Their friendship has been built on his trust in Holmes's methods – suspecting that Holmes is cheating causes Watson great pain because of the depth of his regard for Holmes.*
2: *Holmes apologises for upsetting Watson even though he has done nothing wrong.*		
3: *When Holmes explains his thought processes, Watson is quick to apologise for his misunderstanding.*		

❽ Write up **point 1** into a **paragraph** below, in your own words. Remember to include what you infer from the evidence, or the writer's effects:

....

....

....

....

....

❾ Now, choose **one** of your **other points** and write it out as another **paragraph** here:

....

....

....

....

....

PROGRESS LOG [tick the correct box]   Needs more work ☐   Getting there ☐   Under control ☐

Contexts

QUICK TEST ✔

❶ Tick the **correct box** about the novella's **context** to **finish each statement**:

a) *The Sign of the Four* was written during the reign of:

King Henry VII ☐   Queen Victoria ☐   Queen Elizabeth I ☐

b) India, a country featured in the novella, was ruled at that time by:

the French ☐   the Chinese ☐   the British ☐

c) Women at this time were not allowed to be:

police officers ☐   writers ☐   teachers ☐

d) The British at the time of the novella often viewed foreign people as:

helpful ☐   musical ☐   inferior ☐

e) Punts, skiffs and steam launches are all kinds of:

shops ☐   shoes ☐   boats ☐

f) Jonathan Small drops the Agra treasure into the river:

Clyde ☐   Thames ☐   Severn ☐

THINKING MORE DEEPLY ?

❷ Write **one** or **two sentences** in response to each of these questions:

a) How does the fact that Britain had a global empire at this time have an impact on the characters in the novella?

....

....

....

....

b) What kind of working-class jobs are depicted in the novella?

....

....

....

....

c) In what ways do crime and poverty seem to be linked in the novella?

....

....

....

....

EXAM PREPARATION: WRITING ABOUT THE PRESENTATION OF WOMEN **A03**

Read the section of Chapter 9 from *'I took our mongrel accordingly'* to *'this dreadful and unfounded charge.'* (pp. 78–9)

Question: How does Conan Doyle depict Miss Morstan as a marginalised woman in this extract?

Think about:

- How Miss Morstan reacts to Watson's news
- Watson's feelings about Miss Morstan

❸ Complete this table:

Point/detail	Evidence	Effect or explanation
1: *Watson deliberately leaves out details of Bartholomew Sholto's gruesome death.*	*'I said nothing of the exact manner and method of it'*	*Watson assumes that, as she is a woman, Miss Morstan should not be spoken to about violent behaviour as it would be upsetting for her.*
2: *Mrs Forrester and Miss Morstan retell the story in the style of a fairy tale.*		
3: *Miss Morstan is presented as full of concern, but unable to contribute to the investigation in any practical way.*		

❹ Write up **point 1** into a **paragraph** below in your own words. Remember to include what you infer from the evidence, or the writer's effects:

....

....

....

....

❺ Now, choose **one** of your **other points** and write it out as another **paragraph** here:

....

....

....

....

....

PROGRESS LOG [tick the correct box]   Needs more work ☐   Getting there ☐   Under control ☐

Settings

QUICK TEST

1 Look at the illustrations below. Then write the **names of characters** and **two events** linked to each **location**. Try to use events from the beginning, middle and end of the novella:

221B Baker Street

Characters: ....

....

Events: ....

....

Mordecai Smith's boat hire

Characters: ....

....

Events: ....

....

Mrs Forrester's house, Lower Camberwell

Characters: ....

....

Events: ....

....

Thaddeus Sholto's house, Brixton

Characters: ....

....

Events: ....

....

Pondicherry Lodge, Upper Norwood

Characters: ....

....

Events: ....

....

THINKING MORE DEEPLY

❷ Write **one** or **two sentences** in response to each of these questions about the settings of the novella. Include a comment on the **writer's effects**:

a) Explain how Thaddeus Sholto's home reflects colonial aspects of Victorian society.

....

....

....

b) Find two settings that reflect lower-class lives in Victorian London.

....

....

....

c) Write down three details that make India and the Andaman Islands appear strange or exciting.

....

....

....

❸ **Read these descriptions** and **explain** how Conan Doyle uses **imagery** to bring different aspects of London to life:

a) *'interminable lines of new staring brick buildings,– the monster tentacles which the giant city was throwing out into the country'* (p. 22)

....

....

....

b) *'How sweet the morning air is! See how that one little cloud floats like a pink feather from some gigantic flamingo.'* (p. 63)

....

....

....

c) *We flashed past barges, steamers, merchant-vessels, in and out, behind this one and round the other. Voices hailed us out of the darkness'* (p. 95)

....

....

....

....

PROGRESS LOG [tick the correct box]   Needs more work ☐   Getting there ☐   Under control ☐

Practice task

❶ First, **read** this **exam-style** task:

Question: How does Conan Doyle present the theme of wealth in *The Sign of the Four*?

Consider at least three characters and the way that wealth and money affect their behaviour.

❷ Begin by circling the **key words** in the **question** above.

❸ Now complete this table, noting down **3–4 key points** with **evidence** and the **effect** created:

Point	Evidence/quotation	Effect or explanation

❹ **Draft your response**. Use the space below for your first paragraph(s) and then continue onto a sheet of paper:

Start: *The theme of wealth, money and riches affects many characters in the novella in a range of different ways. The first character I will explore is ...*

PART FIVE: FORM, STRUCTURE AND LANGUAGE

Form

QUICK TEST ✓

❶ **Tick** the correct **answer** about the **form** of the novella to **finish the statement**:

a) *The Sign of the Four* is written in the:

first person ☐   second person ☐   third person ☐

b) *The Sign of the Four* is:

an early romance ☐   a comedy ☐   a detective novel ☐

c) The narrator of the novella is:

Watson ☐   Holmes ☐   Miss Morstan ☐

d) A novella is half way between a short story and a:

play ☐   poem ☐   novel ☐

e) *The Sign of the Four* appeals to the Victorian interest in:

science ☐   animal welfare ☐   magic ☐

THINKING MORE DEEPLY ?

❷ Write **one** or **two sentences** in response to each of these questions:

a) How does Jonathan's Small's detailed account of his life in India in Chapter 12 add to the story of the novella?

....
....
....
....

b) Watson sometimes finds Holmes puzzling. How does Conan Doyle use Watson as a narrator to show different aspects of Holmes's personality?

....
....
....
....

c) In what ways is *The Sign of the Four* a mystery novel? Pick a scene from the novella to explain in what ways Conan Doyle has made the scene mysterious or intriguing for the reader.

....
....
....

PROGRESS LOG [tick the correct box]   Needs more work ☐   Getting there ☐   Under control ☐

Structure

QUICK TEST ✔

❶ Complete this **gap-fill paragraph** about the **structure** of *The Sign of the Four* adding the **correct or suitable** information:

The title of the novella immediately raises questions; who are ………………………… and what

is their …………………….. ? The book opens with Holmes injecting himself with cocaine which

would have been as ……………………………….. for Victorian readers as modern readers. The

first part of the novella sets up a number of seemingly ………………………… puzzles and the

second half of the novella gradually …………………………. the mysteries through a series of

complex plot points. The novella's ………………………. chapters cover many aspects of 'modern'

Victorian life, such as the new police service, the overseas colonies and new scientific approaches

to crime detection. Having ………………… as narrator allows the reader to solve the clues at the

same time as this character does.

THINKING MORE DEEPLY ?

❷ It is important that you can **explain the solutions** to the **puzzles** faced by Holmes and Watson in the novella. For each of these puzzles, write down the answer in a sentence or two:

a) How is Bartholomew Sholto killed?

....

....

....

....

b) Who or what caused the disappearance of Captain Morstan?

....

....

....

....

c) Why can no one find Mordecai Smith's river boat, the Aurora?

....

....

....

....

PROGRESS LOG [tick the correct box]   Needs more work ☐   Getting there ☐   Under control ☐

EXAM PREPARATION: WRITING ABOUT PLOT STRUCTURE

Read from *'Major Sholto was the hardest hit.'* to *'Captain Morstan nodded.'* (pp. 124–5)

Question: How does Conan Doyle use Jonathan Small's testimony in this extract to fill the gaps in the reader's knowledge?

Think about:

- How Conan Doyle has structured the novella so that information is often withheld
- How the reader discovers a shocking side to Captain Morstan and Major Sholto

3 Complete this table:

Point/detail	Evidence	Effect or explanation
1: *Conan Doyle uses a plot device of accident/coincidence to structure the account; by chance, Small overhears Sholto and Morstan discussing their losses.*	*The two men are not careful about keeping their secrets – 'the major was raving about his losses' and they drink 'a good deal'.*	*This may surprise the reader who may have assumed that Sholto and Morstan were innocent victims; this scene reveals their much darker side.*
2: *Conan Doyle answers the question as to why Small approached the two men: in the days of revolution in India, it was easy for treasure to be taken.*		
3: *Conan Doyle presents Small's account of his time in India by using reported speech in speech marks.*		

4 Write up **point 1** into a **paragraph** below in your own words. Remember to include what you infer from the evidence, or the writer's effects:

....

....

....

....

....

5 Now, choose **one** of your **other points** and write it out as another paragraph here:

....

....

....

....

....

....

....

PROGRESS LOG [tick the correct box]   Needs more work ☐   Getting there ☐   Under control ☐

Language

QUICK TEST

❶ **Match** these **words/expressions** associated with characters' jobs with their **meaning**. Try not to check in the book first:

Word:	Meaning:
a) governess	a boy or girl who makes money from running errands
b) pawnbroker	a person who guards the door to an important place
c) street Arab	a person who lends money based on valuable items that people deposit with them
d) porter	a servant in charge of running a house, including meals and cleaning
e) boatman	a person who buys and transports valuable items
f) merchant	a young woman who teaches in a private house
g) housekeeper	a person who hires and sails boats

THINKING MORE DEEPLY

❷ Conan Doyle uses different sentence types, vocabulary and punctuation in order to convey different personalities in the novella. For each of the **quotes** in the table, **explain** what the **language** is conveying about the **character**:

Name of character	Quotation	Effect on character
1: *Sherlock Holmes*	'To the trained eye there as much difference between the black ash of a Trichonopoly and the white fluff of birds'-eye as there is between a cabbage and a potato.'	
2: *Thaddeus Sholto*	'"A doctor, eh?" cried he, much excited. "Have you your stethoscope? Might I ask you – would you have the kindness? I have grave doubts as to my mitrial valve"'	
3: *Wiggins (of the Baker Street Irregulars)*	'"Got your message, sir," said he, "and brought 'em on sharp. Three bob and a tanner for tickets."'	

❸ Conan Doyle often portrays personalities and their emotions through his choice of **verbs**. In the following quotations, **explain** what the underlined verbs are conveying to the reader:

a) 'I could not but observe that as she took the seat which Sherlock Holmes placed for her, her lip <u>trembled</u>, her hand <u>quivered</u> … ' (p. 11)

....

b) '"Don't promise too much, Mr. Theorist,– don't promise too much!" <u>snapped</u> the detective.' (p. 50)

....

c) '"Justice!" <u>snarled</u> the ex-convict. "A petty justice!"' (p. 107)

....

d) 'Tonga thought he had done something very clever in killing him, for when I came up by the rope I found him <u>strutting</u> about as proud as a peacock.' (p. 130)

....

❹ Conan Doyle uses a range of **vocabulary** and **technical words** to convey Sherlock Holmes's scientific understanding. **Pick three words** or **phrases** from the following extract that you think shows Holmes's great knowledge and **write a sentence** to explain why you chose each word:

Holmes shook his head. 'Look at his long letters,' he said. 'They hardly rise above the common herd. That d might be an a, and that I an e. Men of character always differentiate their long letters, however illegibly they write. There is a vacillation in his k's and self-esteem in his capitals. I am going out now. I have some few references to make. Let me recommend this book,– one of the most remarkable ever penned. It is Winwood Reade's "Martyrdom of Man."' (p. 16)

a) _____ I picked this word because _____

_____

_____

b) _____ I picked this word because _____

_____

_____

c) _____ I picked this word because_____

_____

PROGRESS LOG [tick the correct box]   Needs more work ☐   Getting there ☐   Under control ☐

EXAM PREPARATION: WRITING ABOUT CONAN DOYLE'S USE OF LANGUAGE **A02**

Read the section when Watson and Miss Morstan open the treasure box only to find it is empty, from *'What a pretty box!'* to *'from my very heart.'* (pp. 104–5)

Question: What language techniques does Conan Doyle use to convey the dramatic nature of the opening of the box?

Think about:

- The description of the box
- Watson's first-person voice

⑤ Complete this table:

Technique	Example	Effect
1: *Unusual or foreign words*	*'Benares metal-work'* and *'the image of a sitting Buddha'*	*The reader is reminded that this is a very valuable box that has travelled from a long way overseas and has a colonial past.*
2: *Use of speech*		
3: *Watson's use of figurative language*		

⑥ Write up **point 1** into a **paragraph** below in your own words. Remember to include what you infer from the evidence, or the writer's effects:

....

....

....

....

⑦ Now, choose **one** of your **other points** and write it out as **another paragraph** here:

....

....

....

....

....

....

PROGRESS LOG [tick the correct box]   Needs more work ☐   Getting there ☐   Under control ☐

Practice task

❶ First, read this **exam-style** task:

Read the description of Watson's feelings for Miss Morstan after they have visited Pondicherry Lodge, from *'The police had brought a cab with them'* to *'the wild, dark business which had absorbed us.'* (pp. 53–4)

Question: What language techniques does Conan Doyle use to convey the dramatic nature of the opening of the box?

❷ Begin by circling the **key words** in the **question** above.

❸ Now, complete this table, noting down **3–4 key points** with **evidence** and the **effect** created:

Point	Evidence/quotation	Meaning or effect

❹ **Draft your response.** Use the space below for your first paragraph(s) and then continue onto a sheet of paper:

Start: *In this section there are several ways that Conan Doyle conveys Watson's feelings for Miss Morstan. Firstly, ...*

PROGRESS LOG [tick the correct box]   Needs more work ☐   Getting there ☐   Under control ☐

PART SIX: PROGRESS BOOSTER

Expressing and explaining ideas (A01)

❶ How well can you express your ideas about *The Sign of the Four*? Look at this grid and tick the level you think you are currently at:

Level	How you respond	What your spelling, punctuation and grammar are like	Tick
High	• You analyse the effect of specific words and phrases very closely (i.e. 'zooming in' on them and exploring their meaning). • You select quotations very carefully and you embed them fluently in your sentences. • You are persuasive and convincing in the points you make, often coming up with original ideas.	• You use a wide range of specialist terms (words like 'imagery'), excellent punctuation, accurate spelling, grammar, etc.	
Mid/ Good	• You analyse some parts of the text closely, but not all the time. • You support what you say with evidence and quotations, but sometimes your writing could be more fluent to read. • You make relevant comments on the text.	• You use a good range of specialist terms, generally accurate punctuation, usually accurate spelling, grammar, etc.	
Lower	• You comment on some words and phrases but often you do not develop your ideas. • You sometimes use quotations to back up what you say but they are not always well chosen. • You mention the effect of certain words and phrases but these are not always relevant to the task.	• You do not have a very wide range of specialist terms, but you have reasonably accurate spelling, punctuation and grammar.	

SELECTING AND USING QUOTATIONS

❷ Read these two samples from students' responses to a question about how Holmes is presented. Decide which of the three levels they fit best, i.e. **lower** (L), **mid** (M) or **high** (H):

Student A: *Holmes is fascinated rather than frightened by the brutal murder of Bartholomew Sholto. He talks to Watson about it with 'the air of a clinical professor expounding to his class'. This shows that he likes to explain things and does not talk about his feelings. This is something we find out more about later.*

Level? ☐   Why? ....

....

Student B: *Conan Doyle demonstrates Holmes's detached personality using an interesting image when he discusses Bartholomew Sholto's brutal death with 'the air of a clinical professor expounding to his class'. A 'clinical professor' would be able to talk about death without showing any emotion and this leads the reader to see that Holmes is more interested in the facts of Bartholomew's death. The verb 'expounding' could suggest that Holmes is enjoying the discussion because he is speaking in some detail.*

Level: ☐   Why? ....

....

ZOOMING IN – YOUR TURN!

Here is the first part of another student response. The student has picked a good quotation but he hasn't 'zoomed in' on any particular words or phrases:

When Watson, Holmes and Jones plan the capture of Jonathan Small and Tonga, Holmes says 'if we get to their lair' showing that he thinks Small might be hiding.

❸ Pick out one of the **words** or **phrases** the student has quoted and write a further sentence to complete the explanation:

The word/phrase '...', as Holmes uses it, suggests ....

....

....

....

EXPLAINING IDEAS

You need to be precise about the way Conan Doyle gets ideas across. This can be done by varying your use of verbs (not just using 'says' or 'means').

❹ Read this paragraph from a **mid-level** response to a question about Watson's feelings towards Miss Morstan. Circle all the **verbs** that are repeated (not in the quotations):

Conan Doyle shows us Watson's developing love for Miss Morstan when Watson says his 'heart turned as heavy as lead' after learning the treasure is worth half a million pounds. This shows that Watson feels anxious about the huge amount of money that Miss Morstan is set to inherit and says that he has incredibly strong feelings for her.

❺ Now **choose** some of the words below to replace your circled ones:

suggests	implies	tells us	presents	signals	asks
demonstrates	recognises	comprehend	reveals	conveys	

❻ Rewrite your **high-level** version of the paragraph in full below. Remember to mention the **author by name** to show you understand he is **making choices** in how he presents characters, themes and events:

....

....

....

....

....

....

....

....

PROGRESS LOG [tick the correct box]   Needs more work ☐   Getting there ☐   Under control ☐

Making inferences and interpretations

WRITING ABOUT INFERENCES

You need to be able to show you can read between the lines, and make inferences, rather than just explain more explicit 'surface' meanings.

Here is an extract from one student's **high-level** response to a question about Holmes and how he is presented:

In Chapter 1, Watson tries to test Holmes to the limit by asking him to say who owned a watch that Watson gives him. At first Watson 'could hardly keep from smiling at his crestfallen face' when Holmes says the watch is too clean to analyse which shows Watson is amused by Holmes's apparent defeat. But it also conveys to the reader Watson's emotional involvement with Holmes and suggests Watson's lack of full understanding of Holmes's incredible intellect; which is quickly demonstrated when Holmes correctly identifies that the watch belonged to Watson's brother.

❶ Look at the response carefully:
- **Underline** the simple point which explains what Watson does.
- **Circle** the phrase/sentence that develops the first point.
- **Highlight** the phrase/sentence that shows an inference and begins to explore wider interpretations.

INTERPRETING – YOUR TURN!

❷ Read the opening to this student response carefully and then **choose the point** from a), b) or c) which shows **inference** and could lead to a **deeper interpretation**. Remember – interpreting is not guesswork!

Holmes is amused by the newspaper reported that suggests Athelney Jones has solved the case; '"Isn't it gorgeous?" said Holmes, grinning over his coffee cup' (p. 72). This shows he does not mind that he is not mentioned in the report. It also suggests that ...

- a) ..., unlike Athelney Jones, Holmes does not crave publicity or praise.
- b) ... Holmes thinks Athelney Jones is a better detective than he is.
- c) ... Holmes thinks the case is funny.

❸ Now **complete** this **paragraph** about Watson adding your own final sentence which makes inferences or explores wider interpretations:

Watson dislikes the way that Holmes uses cocaine so casually. He describes Holmes's method of taking drugs as a 'performance' which suggests he feels ... .

....

....

....

....

....

PROGRESS LOG [tick the correct box] Needs more work ☐ Getting there ☐ Under control ☐

Writing about context

EXPLAINING CONTEXT

When you write about context you must make sure that what you write is relevant to the task.

Read this comment by a student about Thaddeus Sholto:

The social tastes of the day are reflected in the house that Thaddeus Sholto lives in and it reflects some of the divisions in Victorian society. The priceless items such as the 'tiger-skins' are described as 'Eastern luxury' which contrast greatly with the 'small brick house' of Mordecai Smith and the 'shabby' accommodation of animal handler Mr Sherman. It also reflects the immense money made from colonial trading and overseas exploitation that benefits the Sholto family.

❶ Why is this an **effective paragraph** about **context**? Select a), b) or c):

   a) It explains how Thaddeus Sholto does not care about the poor.

   b) It makes the link between Thaddeus Sholto's home and the context of imperial wealth.

   c) It tells us what houses looked like in the nineteenth century.

EXPLAINING – YOUR TURN!

❷ Now read this **further paragraph**, and complete it by **choosing a suitable point** related to context, selecting from a), b) or c) below:

The relationship between Watson and Miss Morstan is a key aspect of the novella and reveals to the reader some of the Victorian attitudes towards women at that time. Watson is a typical Victorian man; even though he admires Miss Morstan's intelligence, he also finds her vulnerability and helplessness appealing. Holmes, on the other hand, declares that Miss Morstan 'had a decided genius' that helps to solve the case (p. 132). An expectation that women should be quiet and passive is also shown when Watson presents ...

   a) *... Miss Morstan listening with 'parted lips and shining eyes' at his story about the chase down the Thames.*

   b) *... himself saying to Holmes, 'Have you any reason to be dissatisfied with my choice?' during a discussion of marriage to Miss Morstan.*

   c) *... Miss Morstan and Mrs Forrester as ' two graceful, clinging creatures' which conveys their need to hold each other in fear as women unable to participate in a criminal investigation directly.*

❸ Now, **write a paragraph** about how the unequal position of women in Victorian society affects the way that female characters such as Miss Morstan and Mrs Smith are presented by Conan Doyle (for example, look at the way that Miss Morstan is described as 'angelic'):

....

....

....

....

PROGRESS LOG [tick the correct box]   Needs more work ☐   Getting there ☐   Under control ☐

Structure and linking of paragraphs

Paragraphs need to demonstrate your points clearly by:

- Using **topic sentences**
- Focusing on **key words** from quotations
- Explaining their **effect** or meaning

❶ Read this **model paragraph** in which a student explains how Conan Doyle presents Major Sholto:

Conan Doyle presents Major Sholto as an outwardly upstanding member of the British army who in reality has a vicious and selfish nature. When Jonathan Small discloses the secret of the Agra treasure, Sholto is presented as trying to speak 'in a cool, careless way, but his eyes were shining with excitement and greed'. The use of the word 'shining' suggests the extent of Sholto's desperation to obtain the treasure.

Look at the response carefully:

- **Underline** the topic sentence which explains the main point about Major Sholto.
- **Circle** the word that is picked out from the quotation.
- **Highlight** or put a tick next to the part of the last sentence which explains the word.

❷ Now read this **student's paragraph** explaining how Conan Doyle presents Holmes:

We find out about Holmes when he says 'I am delighted to have them' as he is holding Tonga's poisoned darts. This seems to be an unusual reaction but it shows the reader that the thoughtful Holmes has realised he has lessened the danger for other people

> **Expert viewpoint:** This paragraph is unclear. It does not begin with a topic sentence explaining how Conan Doyle presents Holmes and does not zoom in on any key words that tell us what Holmes is like.

Now **rewrite the paragraph**. Start with a **topic sentence**, and pick out a **key word** or **phrase** to 'zoom in' on, then follow up with an **explanation** or **interpretation**:

Conan Doyle presents Holmes as ... .

....

....

....

....

....

....

....

....

....

| **PROGRESS LOG** [tick the correct box] | Needs more work ☐ | Getting there ☐ | Under control ☐ |

It is equally important to make your **sentences link together** and your **ideas follow on** fluently from each other. You can do this by:

- Using a **mixture of short and long sentences** as appropriate
- Using words or phrases that help **connect** or **develop** ideas

❸ Read this **model paragraph** by one student writing about Jonathan Small and how he is presented:

Conan Doyle presents Small initially as a minor criminal but we learn more about him throughout the novella. He is first described as a 'rover' which meant someone who could not settle easily. He suffers the hardship of losing a leg in India but secures a job as a plantation manager. This suggests developing maturity and perseverance. Small finally admits that his capture and the loss of the treasure made him 'half mad' which implies that the treasure has caused him as much misery as it does to Bartholomew Sholto and Miss Morstan.

Look at the response carefully:

- **Underline** the topic sentence which introduces the main idea.
- **Underline** the short sentence which sums up the ideas so far.
- **Circle** any words or phrases that link ideas such as 'who', 'but', 'implying', 'which', etc.

❹ Read this **paragraph** by another student also commenting on how Jonathan Small is presented:

Conan Doyle gives us a vivid picture of Jonathan Small's life. This can be seen when he describes his experiences in India. Small says 'In Worcestershire the life of a man seems a great and sacred thing; but it is very different when there is fire and blood all around you'. This gives the impression he is changed by his circumstances. It suggests he has gained a different attitude to death. He has to make difficult decisions and do terrible things to survive.

Expert viewpoint: The candidate has understood how the character's nature is revealed. However, the paragraph is rather awkwardly written. It needs improving by linking the sentences with suitable phrases and joining words such as: 'where', 'in', 'as well as', 'who', 'suggesting', 'implying'.

Rewrite the paragraph, improving the **style**, and also try to add a **concluding sentence** summing up Jonathan Small's experiences. Start with the same **topic sentence**, but extend it:

Conan Doyle gives us a vivid picture of Jonathan Small's life … ....

....

....

....

....

....

....

....

PROGRESS LOG [tick the correct box]   Needs more work ☐   Getting there ☐   Under control ☐

Writing skills

Here are a number of **key words** you might use when writing in the exam:

Content and structure	Characters and style	Linguistic features
chapter	character	metaphor
scene	role	personification
quotation	minor character	juxtaposition
sequence	dramatic	irony
dialogue	comedy	repetition
climax	villainous	symbol
development	humorous	foreshadowing
description	sympathetic	euphemism

❶ **Circle** any you might find difficult to spell, and then use the 'Look, Say, Cover, Write, Check' method to learn them. This means: **look** at the word; **say** it out loud; then **cover** it up; **write** it out; uncover and **check** your spelling with the correct version.

❷ Create a **mnemonic** for five of your difficult spellings. For example:

symbol: **s**even **y**oung **m**en **b**rought **o**range **l**ions

Or …

break the word down: MET- A- PHOR

a) ....

b) ....

c) ....

d) ....

e) ....

❸ Circle any **incorrect spellings** in this paragraph and then rewrite it:

At the begining of Chapter Four, Conan Doyle discribes the unusual appearence of Thaddeus Sholto who appears to be terrified. He 'writhed his hands together' and his face is in 'perpatual', or continuous, movement. This builds the tention as the reader does not know why Thaddeus is in such a nervous state and what information he will reveal to the charachters.

....

....

....

....

....

....

Punctuation can help make your meaning clear.

Here is one response by a student commenting on Conan Doyle's presentation of Tonga. Check for correct use of:

- Apostrophes
- Speech marks for quotations and emphasis
- Full stops, commas and capital letters

When Tonga and Jonathan Small are close to being arrested, Watson observes tonga in close detail. Watson describes Tonga as an 'unhallowed dwarf'. The word unhallowed means that Tonga is unholy. Conan Doyle's choice of words here shows that Watson is making a moral judgement the word 'dwarf' is also a comment on Tongas short stature that suggests he is an unnatural creature.

❹ Rewrite it **correctly** here:

....

....

....

....

....

....

❺ It is better to use the **present tense** to describe what is happening in the novella.

Look at these two extracts. Which one uses tenses consistently and accurately?

Student A: *Conan Doyle starts and ends the novella with Holmes using cocaine to help him through the periods of boredom that set in when he is not solving cases. Holmes says he could try to be a 'loafer' at these times but instead feels that it is a period of 'stagnation' because it is lacking the stimulation that his brain requires.*

Student B: *Conan Doyle started and ends the novella with Holmes using cocaine to help him through the periods of boredom that set in when he is not solving cases. Holmes says he could try to be a 'loafer' at these times but instead feels that it is a period of 'stagnation' because it was lacking the stimulation that his brain requires.*

❻ Now look at this further paragraph. Underline or circle all the **verbs** first:

Watson tested Holmes at the start of the novella by handing him a watch to analyse, but he thinks Holmes is making a 'lame' excuse when Holmes complained initially that the watch is too clean to have any clues on it. When Holmes correctly deduced that the watch belongs to Watson's brother, Watson regretted his lack of 'faith' in Holmes's remarkable skills.

Now **rewrite** it using the **present tense** consistently:

....

....

....

....

....

....

PROGRESS LOG [tick the correct box]   Needs more work ☐   Getting there ☐   Under control ☐

Tackling exam tasks

DECODING QUESTIONS

It is important to be able to identify **key words** in exam tasks and then quickly generate some ideas.

Read this task and notice how the **key words** have been underlined:

Question: _In what ways_ does _Watson respond_ to _Holmes throughout the novella?_

Write about:

- How Watson responds to Holmes both <u>at the start</u>, and <u>as the novella progresses</u>
- How Conan Doyle <u>presents Watson</u> by the <u>way he writes</u>

❶ Now do the same with this task, i.e. **underline** the **key words**:

Question: _How does Conan Doyle present family relationships in the novella?_

Write about:

- The different families, such as the Morstans and the Sholtos
- How Conan Doyle presents ideas about family ties and tensions

GENERATING IDEAS

❷ Now you need to generate ideas quickly. Use the **spider-diagram*** below and add as **many ideas of your own** as you can:

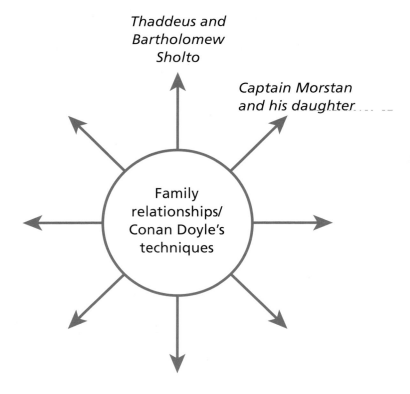

*You could do this as a list if you wish.

Here is the exam-style task from the previous page:

Question: *How does Conan Doyle present family relationships in the novella?*

Write about:

- The different families such as the Morstans and the Sholtos
- How Conan Doyle presents ideas about family ties and tensions.

PLANNING AN ESSAY

❸ **Using the ideas you generated,** write a simple **plan** with at least **five key points** (the first two have been done for you). Check back to your spider diagram or the list you made:

a) *Conan Doyle depicts Thaddeus and Bartholomew having a difficult relationship.*

b) *He depicts Captain Morstan's role as an officer in India and its impact on his daughter Miss Morstan.*

c) ....

....

d ....

....

e) ....

....

❹ Now list **five quotations**, one for each point point (the first two have been provided for you):

a) *'He was the favourite son, you know'*

b) *'My father was an officer in an Indian regiment who sent me home when I was quite a child.'*

c) ....

....

d) ....

....

e) ....

....

❺ Now read this task and **write a plan** of your own, including **quotations**, on a separate sheet of paper:

Read from *'Here's a business!'* to *'How's that?'* (pp. 48–9)

Question: *How is Athelney Jones presented in this scene and how does Holmes respond to him?*

| PROGRESS LOG [tick the correct box] | Needs more work ☐ | Getting there ☐ | Under control ☐ |

Sample answers (A01) (A02) (A03)

OPENING PARAGRAPHS

Read this task:

Question: *How does Conan Doyle depict the relationship between Sherlock Holmes and the police in the novella?*

Now look at these two alternate openings to the essay and read the examiner comments underneath:

Student A

> *Conan Doyle depicts the relationship between Holmes and the police in a range of different ways. Holmes is in a unique position as he is an 'unofficial consulting detective' who does not work for the police but instead moves between private clients and aids the police in solving the most difficult crimes. He sometimes works with Athelney Jones.*

Student B

> *Holmes sometimes helps the police and sometimes works for ordinary people who pay him to solve crimes. Holmes usually works at home. Sometimes he gets on with Athelney Jones and sometimes they disagree.*

Expert viewpoint 1: This is a clear opening paragraph that outlines some of the relationships with the police to be discussed. The quotation helpfully explains Holmes's position. The changeable and uneasy relationship with Athelney Jones could be more clearly outlined.

Expert viewpoint 2: This opening recounts the relationship between Holmes and the police and his private clients and makes a reference to Athelney Jones, without outlining what is to be discussed in the essay, which is the point of the introduction. Holmes's ambiguous and unusual working relationship with the police and Athelney Jones could be explained more clearly.

❶ Which comment belongs to which answer? Match the paragraph (A or B) to the expert's feedback (1 or 2):

   Student A: .... Student B: ....

❷ Now it's your turn. Write the opening paragraph to this task on a separate sheet of paper:

Read from *'By the time that I got out into the grounds Sherlock Holmes was on the roof'* to *'Are you game for a six-mile trudge, Watson?'* (pp. 57–8).

Question: *How is Sherlock Holmes's physical strength and risk-taking depicted here and elsewhere in the novella?*

Think about:

- The risks Holmes takes to find clues
- Watson's reactions to Holmes's behaviour

Remember:

- Introduce the topic in general terms, perhaps **explaining** or '**unpicking**' the key **words** or **ideas** in the task (such as 'depict').
- Mention the **different possibilities** or ideas that you are going to address.
- Use the **author's name**.

WRITING ABOUT TECHNIQUES

Here are two paragraphs in response to a different task, where the students have focused on the writer's techniques. The task is:

Read from *"'A savage!' I exclaimed'* to *'Jonathan Small would give a good deal not to have employed him.'* (pp. 74–5)

Question: *What techniques does Conan Doyle use here to convey Victorian attitudes to foreign races?*

Student A

> *Holmes reads out from a gazetteer a factual account of foreign people. It uses adjectives that describe people as looking deformed – 'naturally hideous'. This tells us that the Victorians made harsh judgements on people such as the Andaman Islanders like Tonga. This reflects the Victorian belief in the importance of the British Empire.*

Student B

> *Conan Doyle here presents Holmes reading from a 'gazetteer' which would have been an index book of different countries, conveying a sense of factual accuracy. However, the vocabulary used in the gazetteer would have a surprising effect on the modern reader with the Andaman Islanders being described using pejorative and emotive adjectives such as 'morose', 'misshapen' and 'intractable'. To the Victorian reader, who would have been proud of the global British empire, this would have been seen as a justification for the harsh treatment of people such as Tonga, who were seen less as human and more as 'a terror' for British travellers.*

Expert viewpoint 1: This response describes the impact that Holmes's words would have on both the Victorian and modern audience; this is effective because a modern audience would have a different response to colonial views of overseas people. It also explores the particular impact of the words of the gazetteer and uses linguistic terms appropriately.

Expert viewpoint 2: This response highlights the implications of Holmes's words. However, the quotation, though appropriate, is not sufficiently embedded in the sentence. There is one instance of the writer's technique mentioned but no others and in the final sentence the point made is not developed and no textual evidence or examples are given.

❸ Which comment belongs to which answer? Match the paragraph (A or B) to the expert's feedback (1 or 2):

Student A: .... Student B: ....

❹ Now, take another **aspect** of the scene and on a separate sheet of paper write your own **paragraph**. You could **comment** on one of these aspects:

- Holmes's comments about Tonga
- The implication of the word 'savage'
- Holmes's use of scientific language

Now read this **lower-level** response to the following task:

Read from 'At that moment, however, as our evil fate would have it' to 'with a half animal fury.' (pp. 95–7)

Question: *How does Conan Doyle bring the capture of Jonathan Small to life for the reader?*

Student response

> *Conan Doyle uses some details that create some excitement, the boat 'creaked with the fierce energy that was driving us along'. This means that the boat was going really quickly and that is exciting for the reader because it might be dangerous.*
>
> *Watson says he is used to hunting but this is the fastest chase he has ever been on. The appearance of Tonga is also shocking in the detail Watson uses.*

Expert viewpoint: The quotation in paragraph 1 is well chosen and gives us a sense of the boat's speed and the intensity of the chase, but there is no an attempt to embed it in a sentence. Nor is there any exploration in either paragraph of the effect the chase is having on Watson, the narrator. Comments on what Conan Doyle intends and his use of language in this scene are needed, and the language the student uses is sometimes too informal, as in, 'going really quickly'.

⑤ **Rewrite** these two **paragraphs** in your own words, improving them by addressing:

- The lack of development of linking of points – no '**zooming in**' on **key words and phrases**
- The lack of **embedded quotations**
- Unnecessary **repetition**, poor **specialist terms** and use of **vocabulary**

Paragraph 1:

In this scene, Conan Doyle depicts the pursuit of Jonathan Small as ....

....

and also ....

....

This implies that ....

....

Paragraph 2:

Watson's response to the chase is at first ....

....

However, ...

....

This links to ....

....

....

A FULL-LENGTH RESPONSE

⑥ Write a **full-length response** to this exam-style task on a separate sheet of paper. Answer **both parts** of the question:

Question: *How is Sherlock Holmes presented throughout the novella?*

Write about:

- How Conan Doyle presents Holmes through Watson's first-person narrative
- How Conan Doyle presents Holmes through the reactions of other characters to him

Remember to do the following:

- Plan **quickly** (no more than 5 minutes) what you intend to write, jotting down **four** or **five supporting quotations**.
- Refer closely to the **key words** in the question.
- Make sure you comment on **what** Conan Doyle does, the **techniques** he uses and the **effect** of those techniques.
- Support your points with **well-chosen quotations** or other evidence.
- Develop your points by '**zooming in**' on particular **words** or **phrases** and explaining their **effect**.
- Be **persuasive** and **convincing** in what you say.
- Check carefully for **spelling**, **punctuation** and **grammar**.

PROGRESS LOG [tick the correct box]   Needs more work ☐   Getting there ☐   Under control ☐

Further questions   (A01) (A02) (A03)

❶ In what ways is *The Sign of the Four* a mystery novella?

❷ Write about the way that Conan Doyle presents the city of London in *The Sign of the Four.*

❸ How important is the friendship between Watson and Holmes in the novella?

❹ Explore the relationship between Jonathan Small and Tonga in the novella.

❺ There are several themes in the novella, such as crime, friendship, and wealth and poverty. Which do you think is the most important theme and why? (You can write about a theme not mentioned.)

PROGRESS LOG [tick the correct box]   Needs more work ☐   Getting there ☐   Under control ☐

ANSWERS

NOTE: Answers have been provided for most tasks. Exceptions are 'Practice tasks' and tasks which ask you to write a paragraph or to use your own words or judgement.

PART TWO: PLOT AND ACTION [pp. 8–32]

Chapter 1 [pp. 8–9]

1 a) F; b) T; c) F; d) F; e) F; f) T; g) F; h) NEE

2 a) Holmes says that he takes 'pleasure' (p. 3) from being a detective and he understands that his ability is 'peculiar' (p. 3) or strange. He says he finds 'minutiae' or small details (p. 5) important in his work and never uses 'guess-work' (p. 8).

b) We learn that Watson was in the military and he is still suffering from injuries from 'the Afghan campaign' (p. 2). We also learn that he is a 'medical man' and sees himself as a 'comrade' (p. 2) of Holmes, having already published one account of Holmes's cases.

c) Holmes says he finds cocaine 'stimulating' (p. 2) although he knows this is 'artificial' (p. 2). Holmes says he needs this stimulation when he has no other work to do, because otherwise he finds everyday life 'dreary' and 'dismal' (p. 9).

3

Point/detail	Evidence	Effect or explanation
1: Watson hates seeing Holmes injecting himself with cocaine.	'from day to day I had become more irritable at the sight, and my conscience swelled nightly within me'	Conan Doyle shows that Watson worries about Holmes both in the day and 'nightly' revealing how much he cares for his friend.
2: Watson understands that he has a complex relationship with Holmes.	'I speak not only as one comrade to another, but as a medical man'	'Comrade' suggests an equal and friendly relationship but, as a medic, Watson feels responsible for Holmes's physical and mental welfare.
3: Watson is reluctant to upset Holmes by questioning him, even if he does not always understand him.	'the experience which I had had of his many extraordinary qualities, all made me diffident and backward in crossing him'	Watson says he is 'diffident' which means hesitant or cautious when it comes to questioning Holmes.

Chapter 2 [pp. 10–11]

1 young; Watson; India; quiet/sad/lonely; pearl; birthday; justice/information; excitedly/eagerly

2 a) Ten years earlier, in 1878, Captain Morstan had telegraphed his daughter asking her to meet him in London on his return from his work in India, with a message of 'kindness and love' (p. 12). However, he did not appear at the hotel where he was staying and Miss Morstan never heard from him again.

b) Holmes is impressed with Miss Morstan because he says she has the 'correct intuition' (p. 14) to bring him the information that he needs for her case. This includes the letters and boxes from which Holmes can work out that the handwriting is 'disguised' (p. 14).

c) Chapter 2 makes several references to British companies working abroad and the British Army such as the '34th Bombay Infantry' (p. 13). It also refers to pearls and 'curiosities' (p. 13) from the 'Andaman Islands' (p. 13) which are in the Indian Ocean and were owned by the British at this time.

3

Point/detail	Evidence	Effect or explanation
1: Conan Doyle shows that Watson cannot concentrate on his book.	'my thoughts were far from the daring speculations of the writer'	Watson describes the book as 'daring', but even so he thinks more about Miss Morstan. The reader might infer that Waton's real life is actually more exciting than the book he is reading.
2: Conan Doyle suggests that Watson and Miss Morstan are compatible because of their ages.	'when youth has lost its self-consciousness and become a little sobered by experience'	Watson, as an older man, is also aware of how his life 'experience' has made him more cautious, and so he sees that he has something in common with Miss Morstan.
3: Watson realises his romantic feelings about Miss Morstan are very different from Holmes's feelings.	'Watson repeats Holmes's dismissive attitude towards Miss Morstan; 'She was a unit, a factor, – nothing more.' This contrasts with Watson's own 'imagination' about his future with her.	The word 'unit' used by Holmes suggests he sees Miss Morstan in a very scientific way and has little interest in her as a person.

Chapter 3 [pp. 12–13]

1 a) the death of Major Sholto; b) puts a revolver in his pocket; c) in Captain Morstan's pocket book; d) crowded and busy; e) all the names of the roads; f) a Hindoo servant

2 a) Holmes searches though the 'back files of the Times' (p. 17) newspaper to obtain more information about Captain Morstan. He uses a 'double lens' (p. 19) to examine the paper from Captain Morstan and makes notes in his notebook so that he does not miss any details, and sits in silence in the coach so that he can think carefully.

b) Watson is sensitive to Miss Morstan's anxiety and so he tries to 'cheer and amuse her', but he confuses words and tells her he fired a 'double-barrelled tiger cub' (p. 21) from his tent.

c) The house is a long way from the city and appears to be isolated. The door is answered immediately which is surprising in a large house. The Hindoo servant is wearing traditional Indian dress and so would have been an unusual sight in Victorian England.

3

Point/detail	Evidence	Effect or explanation
1: The weather seems unusually dark.	'It was a September evening, and not yet seven o'clock, but the day had been a dreary one'	This is an example of pathetic fallacy, where the darkness reflects the 'fog' that the characters are in as they try to solve the mysteries.
2: The streetlights do not seem able to lift the darkness of the early evening.	'the lamps were but misty splotches of diffused light'	The word 'splotches' suggests the street lights give out light randomly, as if the darkness of the evening is too powerful to dispel.

3: The people of London are described as being ghostly and strange.	'they flitted from the gloom into the light, and so back into the gloom once more'	The verb 'flitted' suggests that the people of London move unnaturally quickly, even though this is just a trick of the light. This creates an unsettling mood.

Chapter 4 [pp. 14–15]

1 Thaddeus; anxious/nervous; Captain Morstan; Major; treasure; Bartholomew; Pondicherry

2 a) Thaddeus Sholto is striking in appearance with his bald head that sticks out from his red hair 'like a mountain-peak from fir-trees' (p. 23). Watson says he is 'callous' (p. 24) in the way he casually talks about Captain Morstan's death, although Thaddeus seems anxious and claims that his health is 'fragile' (p. 32).

b) We learn that whatever 'the sign of the four' is, it is connected to Major Sholto. On the night after his death, Major Sholto's home is burgled (although nothing is taken) and 'a torn piece of paper' (p. 30) with 'the sign of the four' written on it is pinned to the dead man's chest.

c) The brothers are twins and have no other siblings which makes them close. Thaddeus seems nervous of Bartholomew, claiming 'he is a terrible fellow when he is angry' (p. 26). Thaddeus suggests his brother can be greedy about material wealth like their father, and so they should approach him carefully.

3

Point/detail	Evidence	Effect or explanation
1: Conan Doyle creates a mystery around the location of Captain Morstan's body.	Major Sholto takes the advice of his servant and deliberately conceals the dead body, using the euphemism 'put him away'.	This is a callous act by Major Sholto which ensures that Miss Morstan will never be able to find her father's body and deepens the mystery around the treasure.
2: Major Sholto himself does not reveal the location of the treasure as he dies mid-sentence.	'The treasure is hidden in–'	This incomplete sentence is an example of a 'cliff-hanger' which ensures that the revelation of where the treasure lies is held back. This adds a mystery to the story.
3: A terrifying and unidentified face appears at the window just as Major Sholto is about to explain where the treasure is.	'a bearded, hairy face, with wild cruel eyes'	The 'hairy' face suggests a person who may be rough and desperate – but the identity of this man (Jonathan Small) is not revealed until much later in the story, extending the mystery for several chapters.

Chapter 5 [pp. 16–17]

1 a) McMurdo and Sherlock Holmes; **b)** Bartholomew Sholto; **c)** Dr Watson and Miss Morstan; **d)** Sherlock Holmes; **e)** Bartholomew Sholto; **f)** Dr Watson; **g)** Thaddeus Sholto

2 a) In this chapter Watson finds himself holding hands with Miss Morstan in 'their hour of trouble' (p. 37) as they sense danger in Pondicherry Lodge. Watson says they behaved 'instinctively' (p. 37) out of love for each other, even though neither had shown any obvious sign of affection up until that point.

b) Holmes is calm in his reaction with his 'raising of the eyebrows' (p. 40) and his close examination of the dead body. Thaddeus, on the contrary, is described as 'the very picture of terror' (p. 41) as he believes that the police will think that he murdered Bartholomew to steal the treasure.

c) Pondicherry House is a large house with a 'high stone wall topped with broken glass' and an 'iron-clamped door' (p. 34) which suggests it is guarding its contents and inhabitants. It is a gloomy place that Watson says 'struck a chill to the heart' (p. 36)

3

Point/detail	Evidence	Effect or explanation
1: Conan Doyle describes the dead body as appearing in an unnatural manner.	'the master of the house was seated all in a heap, with his head sunk upon his left shoulder'	The phrase 'master of the house' suggests power and control and contrasts greatly with the description 'all in a heap' which would shock the reader.
2: Conan Doyle gives disturbing and contradictory detail.	'that ghastly, inscrutable smile upon his face'	The adjective 'ghastly' conveys Watson's horror at Bartholomew's appearance and 'inscrutable' suggests that there is no easy explanation to be found for his death.
3: The weapon used to kill Bartholomew is sinister in its appearance.	'a brown, close-grained stick, with a stone head like a hammer, rudely lashed on with coarse twine'	The comparison of the weapon to a 'hammer' suggests to the reader the horrific force that the weapon had and the word 'rudely' implies that the weapon was made quickly, possibly in desperation.

Chapter 6 [pp. 18–19]

1 a) T; **b)** F; **c)** T; **d)** F; **e)** T; **f)** F; **g)** T

2 a) The 'wooden-legged man' is identified by Holmes because of the unusual footprints left behind. In Chapter 4, Thaddeus Sholto mentions that Major Sholto was terrified of men with wooden legs, underlining the importance of this detail. We later learn it is Jonathan Small.

b) We learn that Bartholomew was killed by poison, which is what caused the smile on his face because of the 'drawn muscles' (p. 47) reacting to the poison. The poison was delivered by a thorn that Holmes is clear is not an 'English thorn' (p. 48).

c) Athelney Jones is very different from Sherlock Holmes; he is 'stout' and 'red-faced' (p. 48) and he believes that he is a better detective than Holmes because he prefers 'stern facts' to 'theories' (p. 48).

3

Point/detail	Evidence	Effect or explanation
1: Holmes appears to be excited about solving the case.	'rubbing his hands'	The fact that Holmes is 'rubbing his hands' suggests that he is ready to work and is looking forward to it.
2: Holmes has a detached manner, even though the facts of the case are horrific and shocking.	'the air of a clinical professor expounding to his class'	Watson compares Holmes to a teacher or lecturer, which conveys Holmes's confidence and great knowledge. The verb 'expounding' suggests he is explaining the case in great detail.

ANSWERS

3: Holmes enjoys involving Watson in his investigation.	'Could you scale that wall, doctor?'	Holmes asks Watson an impossible question as 'that wall' is incredibly high, but the question makes Watson, and the reader, think about the possible answers to the problem.

Chapter 7 [pp. 20–1]

1 a) she could soon be very rich; b) a labyrinth; c) dog; d) poisoned darts; e) timber-yard

2 a) Miss Morstan lives with her employer Mrs Forrester. They appear to be close, and Mrs Forrester speaks to Miss Morstan with a 'motherly' voice, and Watson describes her as 'an honored friend' (p. 54) to Miss Morstan. The house has servants and is described as bright and 'tranquil' (p. 54) which contrasts with the dark and sinister Pondicherry Lodge.

b) Holmes has read the name of Jonathan Small on the treasure map signed by 'the four'. Holmes deduces that Small must have been a convict which is why Morstan had the map. Holmes also explains that he must be 'middle-aged', 'sunburned' and 'bearded' (p. 63).

c) Holmes refers to his ideas as 'the only hypothesis which covers the facts' (p. 61) and he asks Watson 'Do you follow all this?' (p. 62), suggesting Holmes is confident that he is thinking further ahead than Watson. Holmes also says, 'there is no mystery in that' (p. 63) when Watson asks who is Small's accomplice, as if it is obvious, although he does not reveal the answer at that point.

3

Point/detail	Evidence	Effect or explanation
1: Watson finds himself being treated in a way that he is not used to at all.	Mr Sherman is very rude to Watson.	It is funny for the reader to hear Watson described as 'drunken' as he always behaves sensibly. He is also smartly dressed and unlike a 'vagabone' which creates humour.
2: Mr Sherman uses some non-standard English which contrasts with Watson's more 'educated' speech.	'I have a wiper in the bag, an' I'll drop it on your 'ead'	Conan Doyle portrays Mr Sherman as a humorous character by his accent and slang words, such as 'wiper' and ''ead' as well as through the startling image of dropping a snake out of a bag onto someone's head.
3: Mr Sherman keeps a strange collection of animals in his house.	'Keep clear of the badger; for he bites.'	This is an unusual, wild animal to keep as a pet, but Mr Sherman does not seem to see this which creates humour.

Chapter 8 [pp. 22–3]

1 Toby/the dog; wife; newspapers; Pondicherry Lodge; Baker Street Irregulars/street boys; Aurora; accomplice/helper; violin

2 a) Toby is following the scent of creosote which is very widely used in London; Holmes explains that two scent trails were 'running in opposite directions' (p. 66) and they made the wrong choice. Holmes says Toby is 'not to blame' (p. 66).

b) Holmes changes his speech so that he is more in tune with how Mrs Smith herself talks, calling her son 'Dear little chap!' (p. 67) and saying he has heard 'good reports' of Mordecai Smith's boat. This puts Mrs Smith at her ease and so she shares information with him freely (p. 69).

c) Watson says he is 'limp and weary' (p. 71) after being up all night, whereas Holmes is 'laughing' (p. 71) and serving breakfast. Holmes says he never feels 'tired by work' and only 'idleness exhausts' him (p. 74).

3

Point/detail	Evidence	Effect or explanation
1: Conan Doyle uses a range of details that imply the accomplice is barely human.	The man is referred to as a 'savage' and is linked to 'massacres' and cannibal feasts.	It was not unusual in Conan Doyle's time for the natives of overseas colonies that the British had settled in to be seen as inferior to British or Western people.
2: Conan Doyle describes unusual physical characteristics of the accomplice.	'Diminutive footmarks, toes never fettered by boots'	This would be fascinating to the Victorian reader; the lack of shoes would imply the accomplice is more like an animal than human.
3: Holmes quotes from a scientific journal about foreign tribes which explains that natives of the Andaman Islands are violent.	'the British official have failed to win them over in any degree'	This reminds the reader that the British saw themselves as the 'official' and powerful people overseas, although they often faced strong opposition from the native people of the countries they had taken over.

Chapter 9 [pp. 24–5]

1 a) Mordecai Smith's boat; b) Miss Morstan; c) sailor's clothes; d) Althelney Jones; e) the treasure; f) women

2 a) Miss Morstan is not excited about the treasure and shows 'no sign of elation' (p. 78) at the thought of becoming rich. She says she is more concerned about Thaddeus Sholto's arrest, as he has behaved 'kindly and honorably' towards them (p. 79).

b) Watson begins to worry because Holmes has left the house and he doesn't know where he has gone and wonders if there is some 'flaw' (p. 82) or mistake in Holmes's thinking. Watson wonders if Holmes is too quick to find a 'bizarre explanation' (p. 82) when a simple one is correct.

c) Holmes says he is now recognised by 'the criminal classes' (p. 86) since Watson has written about his detective work, and so a disguise allows him to 'go on the war-path' (p. 86) without being spotted.

3

Point/detail	Evidence	Effect or explanation
1: Conan Doyle shows that it is essential to Holmes that he is completely in charge of events.	Holmes insists that Athelney Jones follows his instructions exactly: 'you must put yourself under my orders'	The modal verb 'must' conveys Holmes's determination and control and the phrase 'under my orders' implies that Holmes is fully in charge.

2: Athelney Jones not only takes Holmes's order, he also asks for further requests.	Athelney Jones asks 'What else?' and comments 'You are the master of the situation.'	The question conveys the fact that the police inspector is fully engaged with Holmes's plans, which contrasts with the way that Conan Doyle presented Athelney Jones earlier in the novella, when he often disagrees with Holmes's ideas.
3: Conan Doyle shows that Holmes is even able to make unusual requests.	Holmes asks that Miss Morstan is the first to open the treasure box before it is handed to the police, which Jones calls 'irregular'.	This conveys to the reader that Holmes is now so well respected that the police are happy to let him follow his own procedures.

Chapter 10 [pp. 26–7]

1 a) T; b) T; c) F; d) T; e) F; f) F; g) T

2 a) Instead of trying to hide the boat, which would have been impossible, Small had taken the boat to a repairer to make some 'trifling change' (p. 92) to it so that it would not be easily recognisable.

b) Watson describes the accomplice as 'the smallest I have ever seen' and he barely seems to believe that he is human, calling him a 'savage, distorted creature' (p. 96) who behaves with 'a half animal fury' (p. 97).

c) When they realise that a poisoned dart has been thrown at them and narrowly missed, Holmes 'smiled at it and shrugged his shoulders' (p. 98) whereas Watson says it 'turned me sick' (p. 98). This shows that Watson is arguably more realistic about the dangers that they have been in through the course of the evening.

3

Point/detail	Evidence	Effect or explanation
1: Conan Doyle conveys excitement through the reckless way that Holmes behaves.	Holmes encourages the crew to sail the boat fast: 'If we burn the boat we must have them!'	Holmes risks setting fire to the boat, but the use of the verb 'must' conveys his desperation.
2: Watson is impressed by the immense power of the boat engines.	'the powerful engines whizzed and clanked, like a great metallic heart'	The simile used here conveys the energy and movement of the engines as they sail along the river.
3: The Aurora is described as speeding ahead of Holmes's boat as if it might get away from them at any time.	'but still the Aurora thundered on'	The verb 'thundered' suggests the enormous power and deafening sound of the boat, implying that it is a difficult chase that could easily go wrong, creating tension for the reader.

Chapter 11 [pp. 28–9]

1 Jonathan Small; cigar; Bartholomew Sholto; Pondicherry Lodge; Tonga; curse; the river; empty

2 a) Jonathan Small, like Watson in the previous chapter, describes Tonga as if he is barely human. He calls him a 'hell-hound' and a 'little devil' (p. 100) which suggests he is evil and animalistic.

b) Athelney Jones resumes criticising Holmes, saying 'you must confess that you cut it rather fine'. Watson comments that he was starting to 'give himself airs' (p. 101) which implies that he was acting as if he was more important than Holmes in the discovery of the treasure.

c) Watson describes the treasure as a 'golden barrier' (p. 104) between himself and Miss Morstan because it made him anxious that he was only interested in marrying her because the treasure could have made her very rich. Without the treasure, Watson can prove he loves her honestly, without any thought of riches.

3

Point/detail	Evidence	Effect or explanation
1: Conan Doyle has presented Miss Morstan as a lonely figure earlier in the novella and this is suggested here too.	She is pictured sitting alone in the window of her home, with an air of 'absorbing melancholy'	The word 'absorbing' conveys the sense that Miss Morstan can be taken over by her sadness or 'melancholy' which is beyond her control.
2: Conan Doyle describes Miss Morstan as a particularly gentle and virtuous young woman.	She wears a 'white diaphonous' dress and only reacts 'coolly' to the recovery of the treasure.	The colour white is usually associated with honesty and goodness; this links to the fact that Miss Morstan is not greedy and has no interest in the value of the treasure.
3: She seems to be a woman who is associated with the home and a quiet, unadventurous life.	She is generally seen to be happiest when she is at home and has regular daily routines involving her employer Mrs Forrester.	This has the effect of presenting Miss Morstan as an ideal woman in the eyes of the typical Victorian gentleman, such as Watson, who would value domesticity and gentleness very highly.

Chapter 12 [pp. 30–1]

1 1 – e; 2 – b; 3 – d; 4 – h; 5 – a; 6 – f; 7 – g; 8 – c

2 a) Jonathan Small throws the treasure into the river because he says that 'no living man' in the world is entitled to the treasure other than himself and the rest of 'the four'. Small regards the river as a 'safe place' (p. 107), especially as it will not be able to fall into the hands of Sholto or Morstan's family.

b) We learn that Major Sholto was a heavy gambler and a drinker who would often spend his days in a mood as 'black as thunder'. Major Sholto eventually loses so much at gambling that he is a 'ruined man' (p. 124) which is when he agrees to help Small recover the Agra treasure.

c) Holmes claims he will never marry because love is an 'emotional thing' and Holmes prefers to keep his 'true cold reason' (p. 132).

3

Point/detail	Evidence	Effect or explanation
1: Conan Doyle begins the passage at a quiet time of the night when little appears to be happening.	'It was dreary work'	This builds tension from a low point because the reader is surprised when Small is attacked by two Sikh men, one of whom holds a 'great knife' to his throat.

2: Conan Doyle describes the moments when Small has a knife at his throat in great detail.	'One of them snatched my firelock up and levelled it at my head'	The verb 'snatched' implies a fast and desperate movement, while the verb 'levelled' suggests precision in the aim of the gun.
3: Conan Doyle increases the tension when the attacker unexpectedly tells Small that the fort is not actually under attack.	There are only two men that have approached Small, and they tell him that 'The fort is safe.' Small has been employed to guard the fort against a rebel army; it is therefore initially confusing that he – a single guard – has been attacked by just two men.	This has the effect of making the reader want to know why the men have attacked Small. Conan Doyle deliberately structures the section so that information is held back for as long as possible, to make the reader want to read further.

PART THREE: CHARACTERS [pp. 33–41]

Who's who? [p. 33]

a) Mrs Forrester/**Miss Morstan's employer**; b) **Miss Morstan**/Captain Morstan's daughter; c) Mrs Hudson/**Sherlock Holmes's landlady**; d) **Dr Watson**/Holmes's closest friend; e) Sherlock Holmes/**Private detective**; f) Athelney Jones/Police detective; g) Thaddeus Sholto/ Son of Major Sholto; h) **Toby**/Tracker dog; i) Jonathan Small/**One of 'the four'**; j) Mr Sherman/**Owner of Toby**; k) **The Baker Street Irregulars**/Street children; l) Tonga/**Accomplice to Jonathan Small**

Sherlock Holmes [p. 34]

1 a) T; b) F; c) T; d) F; e) F; f) F

2

Quality	Moment(s) in novella	Quotation
a) restless	Holmes explains he has to take cocaine to cope with having nothing to do.	'I abhor the dull routine of existence.' (p. 2)
b) rational	Holmes can make logical judgements, such as the fact that the sheet marked 'The sign of the four' has been kept in a pocket book because it is clean on both sides.	'it is evidently a document of importance' (p. 19)
c) unpredictable	Holmes goes out dressed as a sailor without telling Watson what he is doing, and tricks Watson and Athelney Jones.	'I thought my disguise was pretty good' (p. 86)
d) confident	Holmes takes full control of the chase up the river with the police.	'you must act on the line that I point out' (p. 87)
e) highly intelligent	Holmes often refers to writers and academics in his arguments and can make philosophical points related to the cases.	'Winwoode Reade ... remarks that , while the individual man is an insoluble puzzle, in the aggregate he becomes a mathematical certainty' (p. 94)

Dr Watson [p. 35]

1, 2 thoughtful (p. 16); romantic (p. 105); loyal (p. 132); sensitive (p. 11); humble (p. 53)

3 narrates/tells; surgeon/doctor; pain/discomfort; friend/colleague; Miss Morstan; money; brave/important

Miss Morstan [p. 36]

1 a) F; b) T; c) T; d) F; e) NEE; f) T; g) F

2 a) We first meet Miss Morstan when she visits Holmes to ask for help in finding out about the death of her father and the mystery of the pearls.

b) Holmes has been recommended to her by her employer Mrs Forrester.

c) Every year on her birthday Miss Morstan has received a beautiful and valuable pearl in the post.

d) Miss Morstan is fearful about her father because nobody has ever seen him again after he failed to attend a meeting with her ten years earlier.

e) When Watson tells her he was nearly shot with a poisoned dart, Miss Morstan goes pale with fear.

Thaddeus Sholto [p. 37]

1, 2 artistic (p. 23); wronged (p. 36); fair (p. 31); comic (p. 32); kind (p. 31); eccentric (p. 25)

3 Major Sholto; Bartholomew Sholto; unusual/strange; artistic; wrong; Miss Morstan; pearl; Athelney Jones; innocent; treasure

Jonathan Small [p. 38]

1 a) T; b) F; c) T; d) F; e) T; f) NEE; g) F

2

Quality	Moment(s) in novella	Quotation
a) ironic	Small feels it is almost comic that he ended up in prison both in India and in England, despite having the treasure in his grasp.	'I who have a fair claim to nigh upon half a million of money' (p. 101)
b) determined	Small never gives up looking for Major Sholto and the treasure.	'a man who was not to be easily turned from his purpose' (p. 99)
c) passionate	Small grows furious at Athelney Jones's suggestion that it would have been better if he had given up the treasure, rather than throw it in the river.	'his eyes blazed, and the handcuffs clanked together' (p. 108)
d) violent	Small kills the convict-guard at the Andaman Islands by hitting him over the head with his wooden leg.	'I struck him full, and knocked the whole front of his skull in' (p. 128)

Athelney Jones [p. 39]

1 a) Athelney Jones first appears in the novella after Bartholomew Sholto's murder at Pondicherry Lodge.

b) Athelney Jones is a detective who is based at Scotland Yard, London.

c) After the death of Bartholomew Sholto, Athelney Jones arrests everyone in the house.

d) Atheleny Jones criticises Holmes's methods, saying that he is too interested in theories and not facts.

e) Athelney Jones helps in the river chase by agreeing to send police men and boats and to follow Holmes's orders exactly.

f) Although they are professional rivals, Jones and Holmes are generally friendly to each other.

2 impolite – Athelney Jones is quite rude when he describes Holmes's attempt to help him and the police as a 'lecture', implying Holmes was being domineering towards them.

critical – Athelney Jones deliberately suggests that Holmes's method was not as effective as it seemed and the case solving was actually down to 'luck'.

Minor characters [p. 40]

1 a) McMurdo; b) Lal Rao; c) Mrs Forrester; d) Mrs Hudson; e) Wiggins; f) Mr Sherman

2 a) friend and co-conspirator; b) tracked by Small to find the treasure; c) rents Small a boat; d) one of 'the four' in India; e) boss of plantation in India where Small is an 'overseer'; f) the first person that Small tells about the treasure, and who steals the treasure from Small

PART FOUR: THEMES, CONTEXTS AND SETTINGS [pp. 42–50]

Themes [pp. 42–5]

1 Watson; personalities; rational/scientific; risks; amazement/admiration; considerate; Captain Morstan; members of 'the four'

2 a) otherness; b) friendship; c) colonialism; d) wealth; e) revenge

3 a) Conan Doyle's description of the drowning Tonga shows that Watson is more focused on his own reaction to Tonga's appearance than on the horror of his death. Tonga is shown to be less than human when Conan Doyle describes his eyes as 'venomous' because it would make the reader think of a snake or another poisonous creature.

b) Conan Doyle develops our understanding of the friendship between Holmes and Watson here by the way they have the same reaction to Toby the dog following the wrong scent. The word 'simultaneously' implies that they echo each other's movements because they are in sympathy with each other's feelings. The 'uncontrollable' laughter suggests that it is genuine and shared.

4 a) Captain Morstan's crime of helping to steal the Agra treasure was committed out of greed and a need to pay off gambling debts.

b) Jonathan Small falls into a life of crime because he is no longer able to work for the British army in India after the loss of his leg, leading him into a more dangerous and violent life.

c) Sherlock Holmes's approach to solving crime includes looking closely at physical evidence, making notes and thinking carefully and sometimes in unexpected ways.

d) Major Sholto's crime of disposing of Captain Morstan's body has the effect of leaving Miss Morstan devastated by the disappearance of her father, and the breakdown of the relationship between Thaddeus and Bartholomew Sholto.

5 a) Tonga is always presented as being less than human, with Conan Doyle using animalistic vocabulary such as teeth which 'grinned and chattered', and including details such as eating raw meat and worshipping foreign gods. This reflects the way the British easily portrayed the native inhabitants of colonised islands as inferior. Tonga is treated differently to Jonathan Small and is brutally shot, whereas Small is arrested and given a chance to tell his story.

b) Conan Doyle explores the way that twin brothers can display very different personalities despite having an identical appearance and upbringing. Bartholomew is described as following his 'father's custom' (p. 36) of greed: however, Bartholomew suspects his father favoured Thaddeus which made their relationship difficult and ultimately leads to their separation.

c) Miss Morstan is unable to live an independent life because she has no parents or husband to 'look after' her and so she lives with a family as a governess to give her social respectability. She cannot easily find highly paid work or own a house. Watson praises her for being 'angelic' and 'placid' (p. 53) because it was considered more desirable for middle-class women to be quiet and accepting rather than outspoken.

6 a) The adjective 'winning' means friendly and pleasant, and Conan Doyle contrasts this with the description of her crime, which is extremely shocking. The fact the children are described as 'little' emphasises their vulnerability and the seriousness of the crime; the fact that such a seemingly pleasant woman can commit such a terrible crime reflects the theme of duality within a single person.

b) Conan Doyle choses to make the brothers Thaddeus and Bartholomew twins, which would imply to the reader that they could be expected to be particularly close, and is reinforced by the way Thaddeus refers to him as 'Brother'; however, the reference to 'my father's fault' is a euphemism for greed and the desire to hold on to the treasure, reflecting the opposing aspects of the twins' personalities.

c) When Watson finds Holmes's ability to work out information about Watson's brother, it actually causes Watson some emotional distress; Conan Doyle portrays the duality of Holmes and Watson's relationship. Holmes favours the 'abstract' which is connected to rational thought, while Watson is more 'personal' which can lead to 'painful' emotions.

7

Point/detail	Evidence	Effect or explanation
1: *Watson is horrified at the thought that Holmes has tried to deceive him.*	*'you now pretend to deduce this knowledge in some fanciful way'*	*Their friendship has been built on his trust in Holmes's methods – suspecting that Holmes is cheating causes Watson great pain because of the depth of his regard for Holmes.*
2: *Holmes apologises for upsetting Watson even though he has done nothing wrong.*	*'My dear doctor … pray accept my apologies'*	*Holmes uses an affectionate term 'my dear' that he does not use for other characters. He rarely apologises for appearing insensitive, and this shows his great warmth towards Watson.*
3: *When Holmes explains his thought processes, Watson is quick to apologise for his misunderstanding.*	*'I regret the injustice that I did you.'*	*This passage not only demonstrates Holmes's remarkable ability of deduction, but also shows how much the two men care about each other's feelings and will quickly apologise and resolve misunderstandings.*

Contexts [pp. 46–7]

1 a) Queen Victoria; b) the British; c) police officers; d) inferior; e) boats; f) Thames

ANSWERS

2 a) Many of the characters are affected: Jonathan Small finds work as a soldier and then a farm manager in India when he needs to leave home, and Captain Morstan and Major Sholto both have respectable careers in the British army overseas and Major Sholto has acquired 'a considerable sum of money' (p. 26). Furthermore. Watson is still recovering from his time as an army surgeon in Afghanistan with a 'Jezail bullet' (p. 4) still lodged in his leg.

b) Conan Doyle depicts a range of working-class jobs, many of which Sherlock Holmes is very familiar with, such as the 'prize-fighter' (p. 35) McMurdo, the boat-keeping river family of Mordecai Smith who Holmes calls 'people of that sort' (p. 69) and the street children and beggars called the 'Baker Street Irregulars' (p. 73).

c) Crime and poverty are linked in the character of Mordecai Smith, for example, who knowingly helps Jonathan Small for financial gain. Major Sholto is driven to crime by fear of poverty: 'I am a ruined man' (p. 124). However, many poor characters, such as Mr Sherman, appear honest and hardworking, so the link between crime and poverty is not as strong as it might seem.

3

Point/detail	Evidence	Effect or explanation
1: Watson deliberately leaves out details of Bartholomew Sholto's gruesome death.	'I said nothing of the exact manner and method of it'	Watson assumes that, as she is a woman, Miss Morstan should not be spoken to about violent behaviour as it would be upsetting for her.
2: Mrs Forrester and Miss Morstan retell the story in the style of a fairy tale.	'It is a romance!' 'And two knight-errants to the rescue'	Conan Doyle presents the characters as participants in a medieval fairy tale or 'romance' in which women were marginalised and whose roles were to be rescued rather than to be heroes.
3: Miss Morstan is presented as full of concern, but unable to contribute to the investigation in any practical way.	'It is for Mr. Thaddeus Sholto that I am anxious'	Miss Morstan is expected to be passively involved, and as a woman has no power or independent actions.

Settings [pp. 48–9]

1 221B Baker Street

Characters: Holmes, Watson, Miss Morstan, Athelney Jones

Events: Miss Morstan visits Holmes to explain the case of her missing father; Athelney Jones comes here to plan the hunt for the treasure with Holmes and Watson.

Mordecai Smith's boat hire

Characters: Jonathan Small, Holmes, Mrs Smith

Events: Jonathan Small uses this boat-house to hire the Aurora; Holmes speaks to Mrs Smith here when he is trying to trace Jonathan Small.

Mrs Forrester's house, Lower Camberwell

Characters: Miss Morstan, Watson

Events: Watson takes Miss Morstan back to Mrs Forrester's house after the visit to Pondicherry Lodge; Watson later proposes to Miss Morstan in the drawing room.

Thaddeus Sholto's house, Brixton

Characters: Holmes, Watson and Miss Morstan, Thaddeus Sholto.

Events: Holmes, Watson and Miss Morstan visit Sholto's house after meeting his servant at the Lyceum Theatre; Thaddeus chose to

live in an isolated house to avoid 'the rough crowd' of central London (p. 25).

Pondicherry Lodge, Upper Norwood

Characters: Bartholomew Sholto, Tonga, Major Sholto

Events: Major Sholto hides the Agra treasure in a hidden fake room here; Bartholomew Sholto is murdered here by Tonga.

2 a) Thaddeus Sholto's home is full of items that have been brought back from overseas colonies such as 'tiger-skins' and an 'Oriental vase' (p. 24). He employs a 'Hindoo servant' (p. 22) and smokes a 'hookah' (p. 25). This has the effect of making the reader see the power and wealth that the British gained from colonialism.

b) Mr Sherman lives in a 'shabby' house in Lambeth (p. 55); he does not have a servant to answer the door and the house is stuffed full of unusual animals. Mordecai Smith's house at the Thames boat house also reflects a life of poverty, with the six-year-old son asking for 'a shillin' (p. 67).

c) Conan Doyle presents the startling image of Jonathan Small losing his leg to a crocodile in a river in India. Small describes the city of Agra as 'swarming with fanatics and fierce devil-worshippers of all sorts' (p. 111), where the word 'swarming' suggests chaos and excitement, and the Andaman Islands as being 'infested with wild cannibal natives' (p. 123).

3 a) Conan Doyle uses the image of 'monster tentacles' to convey the way that London is growing rapidly and has a life of its own. It also conveys a sense of danger and strangeness to the city.

b) This description reflects the way London can seem beautiful in unexpected ways; the image of the 'gigantic flamingo' not only conveys the deep pink of the morning clouds but also the surreal nature of the scenery.

c) This description of the river Thames conveys its busy and hectic nature through the use of the word 'flashed' and the listing of all the large industrial boats and the unidentified 'voices' that would have been sailing on its waters.

PART FIVE: FORM, STRUCTURE AND LANGUAGE [pp. 51–7]

Form [p. 51]

1 a) first person; **b)** a detective novel; **c)** Watson; **d)** novel; **e)** science

2 a) Jonathan Small's account allows the reader to see more clearly how the British live in India and how the conditions there have led to the theft of the Agra treasure. The Victorian reader would be entertained and maybe shocked by the tales of crocodiles, plantations, Indian palaces and frightening islanders.

b) Using Watson as a narrator gives Conan Doyle an opportunity to present not just the public side but also the domestic side of Sherlock Holmes, such as his love of music and his delight in tricking Athelney Jones and Watson when he enters the house wearing a disguise.

c) The scene when Watson and Holmes visit Pondicherry Lodge in Chapter 5 contains many mysterious elements and unsolved mysteries, such as the 'long, dark thorn' (p. 41) stuck in Bartholomew Sholto, the crude hammer and the ambiguous note left behind.

Structure [pp. 52–3]

1 'the four'; 'sign'; shocking/surprising; unanswerable/impossible; solves/explains; twelve; Watson

2 a) Bartholomew Sholto is found dead in his laboratory where the treasure was kept at Pondicherry Lodge (with a poisoned dart in his skin). He has been killed by Tonga who was able to climb up through the roof.

b) Captain Morstan died of a heart attack which caused him to fall and smash his head during an argument with Major Sholto. Sholto then concealed Morstan's body so that no suspicion would fall on him and to enable him to keep the Agra treasure.

c) Jonathan Small paid for the Aurora to be repainted so that it was unrecognisable.

3

Point/detail	Evidence	Effect or explanation
1: Conan Doyle uses a plot device of accident/ coincidence to structure the account; by chance, Small overhears Sholto and Morstan discussing their losses.	The two men are not careful about keeping their secrets – 'the major was raving about his losses' and they drink 'a good deal'.	This may surprise the reader who may have assumed that Sholto and Morstan were innocent victims; this scene reveals their much darker side.
2: Conan Doyle answers the question as to why Small approached the two men: in the confusing days of revolution in India, it was easy for treasure to be taken.	'the real owner is outlawed and cannot hold property'	The reader would not have guessed that Small offered the treasure to the two men in a desperate attempt to take it out of India safely.
3: Conan Doyle presents Small's account of his time in India by using reported speech in speech marks.	'"It rings true, eh?" said he. "It's good enough to act upon?"'	This level of detail in Small's account allows Conan Doyle to fill in some gaps about the characters of Major Sholto and Captain Morstan because we can hear their voices directly.

Language [pp. 54–7]

1 a) governess – a young woman who teaches in a private house (Miss Morstan); b) pawnbroker – a person who lends money based on valuable items that people deposit with them (Watson's brother); c) street Arab – a boy or girl who makes money from running errands (Wiggins); d) porter – a person who guards the door to an important place (McMurdo); e) boatman – a person who hires and sails boats (Mordecai Smith); f) merchant – a person who buys and transports valuable items (Achmet); g) housekeeper – a servant who would be in charge of running a house, including meals and cleaning (Mrs Hudson)

2

Name of character	Quotation	Effect on character
1: Sherlock Holmes	'To the trained eye there is as much difference between the black ash of a Trichonopoly and the white fluff of birds'-eye as there is between a cabbage and a potato.'	The adjective 'trained' conveys Holmes's previous study, and the knowledge about the details of a tip of a 'Trichonopoly' cigarette reminds the reader of his great attention to detail.

| 2: Thaddeus Sholto | '"A doctor, eh?" cried he, much excited. "Have you your stethoscope? Might I ask you – would you have the kindness? I have grave doubts as to my mitrial valve"' | Thaddeus talks very quickly because he is excited. The range of different punctuation and short sentences, such as 'Might I ask you' with the dash, convey his animated manner. |
| 3: Wiggins (of the Baker Street Irregulars) | '"Got your message, sir," said he, "and brought 'em on sharp. Three bob and a tanner for tickets."' | Conan Doyle conveys Wiggins's accent with how he pronounces the word "em' and he uses slang words for money such as 'tanner' which shows he is a street boy in London. |

3 a) Miss Morstan's fear and anxiety; b) Athelney Jones's annoyance with Holmes; c) Jonathan Small's anger at being arrested; d) Tonga's excitement at killing Bartholomew Sholto

4 a) 'vacillation' is a more scientific way of saying being 'indecisive'; b) 'references' shows that Holmes is undertaking research; c) 'Martyrdom of Man' suggests a difficult/scientific book that Holmes has read

3

Technique	Example	Effect
1: Unusual or foreign words	'Benares metal-work' and 'the image of a sitting Buddha'	The reader is reminded that this is a very valuable box that has travelled from a long way overseas and has a colonial past.
2: Use of speech	'"The treasure is lost," said Miss Morstan calmly.'	Conan Doyle put this observation into Miss Morstan's voice as the treasure would have belonged to her and made her very wealthy.
3: Watson's use of figurative language	'this Agra treasure had weighed me down'	The metaphor shows the reader that Watson had secretly felt anxious that the wealth of the treasure would have prevented him from marrying Miss Morstan – carrying this knowledge was like a heavy weight for him.

PART SIX: PROGRESS BOOSTER [pp. 58–71]

Expressing and explaining ideas [pp. 58–9]

2 Student A: Mid
The student picks a suitable quote and makes relevant comments, but does not analyse the language features used by Conan Doyle or explore the quote in more detail.

Student B: High
The student identifies techniques and provides clear explanation of the effect of Conan Doyle's language on the reader with some detailed exploration of the possible effect of specific words.

3 *The word 'lair', as Holmes uses it, suggests an animal den or burrow which implies that the place where Small and Tonga are hiding may be hidden and unpleasant.*

4 *The repeated verbs are 'shows' and 'says'.*

ANSWERS

5, 6 *Conan Doyle **reveals** Watson's powerful feelings for Miss Morstan when Watson **tells** the reader that 'his heart turned as heavy as lead' after learning the exact amount that Miss Morstan is likely to inherit. The reader would **recognise** that this money would present a huge social gap between the two characters because Watson would be much poorer than Miss Morstan. The simile 'as heavy as lead' **conveys** Watson's immense sadness that solving the case may potentially mean they are never able to marry and **implies** Watson will have to bear the burden of that knowledge.*

Making inferences and interpretations [p. 60]

1 *In Chapter 1, Watson tries to test Holmes to the limit by asking him to say who owned a watch that Watson gives him. At first Watson 'could hardly keep from smiling at his crestfallen face' when Holmes says the watch is too clean to analyse which shows Watson is amused by Holmes's apparent defeat. But it also conveys to the reader Watson's emotional involvement with Holmes and suggests Watson's lack of full understanding of Holmes's incredible intellect; which is quickly demonstrated when Holmes correctly identifies that the watch belonged to Watson's brother.*

2 a) *…, unlike Athelney Jones, Holmes does not crave publicity or praise.*

3 *… that it is a time-consuming and elaborate action that is unnecessary and, to him, undesirable.*

Writing about context [p. 61]

1 b) *It makes the link between Thaddeus Sholto's home and the context of imperial wealth.*

2 c) *… Miss Morstan and Mrs Forrester as 'two graceful, clinging creatures' which conveys their need to hold each other in fear as women unable to participate in a criminal investigation directly.*

Structure and linking of paragraphs [p. 62]

1 *Conan Doyle presents Major Sholto as an outwardly upstanding member of the British army who in reality has a vicious and selfish nature. When Jonathan Small discloses the secret of the Agra treasure, Sholto is presented as trying to speak 'in a cool, careless way, but his eyes were shining with excitement and greed'. The use of the word 'shining' suggests the extent of Sholto's desperation to obtain the treasure.*

2 Possible answer:
Conan Doyle presents Holmes as a detective who always thinks one step ahead of other people which can make his reactions seem surprising or unusual. Watson is horrified at the discovery of the dangerous poisoned darts, but Conan Doyle says that Holmes is 'delighted' to be holding them. This is because Holmes knows that if he has Tonga's darts then Tonga cannot use them to harm other people. However, the word 'delighted' is an unexpected word when applied to such unpleasant items.

3 *Conan Doyle presents Small initially as a minor criminal but we learn more about him throughout the novella. He is first described as a 'rover' which meant someone who could not settle easily. He suffers the hardship of losing a leg in India but secures a job as a plantation manager. This suggests developing maturity and perseverance. Small finally admits that his capture and the loss of the treasure made him 'half mad' which implies that the treasure has caused him as much misery as it does to Bartholomew Sholto and Miss Morstan.*

4 Possible answer:
Conan Doyle gives us a vivid picture of Jonathan Small through the words that Small uses to describe his life. Small is greatly changed by his experiences in India where he is surrounded by 'fire and blood', suggesting death and danger. Conan Doyle implies that it becomes

a man to whom life is no longer 'sacred' because he is forced into committing murder by the extreme circumstances in which he finds himself. This conveys the impression that Jonathan Small is a character who has had to make terrible decisions.

Writing skills [p. 64]

3 *At the **beginning** of Chapter Four, Conan Doyle **describes** the unusual **appearance** of Thaddeus Sholto who appears to be terrified. He 'writhed his hands together' and his face is in '**perpetual**', or continuous, movement. This builds the **tension** as the reader does not know why Thaddeus is in such a nervous state and what information he will reveal to the **characters**.*

4 *When Tonga and Jonathan Small are close to being arrested, Watson observes **Tonga** in close detail. Watson describes Tonga as an 'unhallowed dwarf'. The word '**unhallowed**' means that Tonga is unholy. Conan Doyle's choice of words here shows that Watson is making a moral **judgement**. The word 'dwarf' is also a comment on **Tonga's** short stature that suggests he is an unnatural creature.*

5 Student A

6 *Watson **tests** Holmes at the start of the novella by handing him a watch to analyse, but he **thinks** Holmes **is making** a 'lame' excuse when Holmes **complains** initially that the watch is too clean to have any clues on it. When Holmes correctly **deduces** that the watch **belongs** to Watson's brother, Watson **regrets** his lack of 'faith' in Holmes's remarkable skill.*

Tackling exam tasks [p. 66]

1 Question: How does Conan Doyle present family relationships in the novella?

Write about:

- The different families, such as the Morstans and the Sholtos
- How Conan Doyle presents ideas about family ties and tensions

3, 4

c) *He depicts the family relationship that has developed between Miss Morstan and Mrs Forrester.*

> '… how motherly was the voice in which she greeted her.'
> (p. 54)

d) *He presents the distant family relationship between Watson and his alcoholic brother.*

> '… your brother was often at low water.' (p. 9)

e) *Conan Doyle describes the family of Mordecai Smith.*

> 'I am beginnin' to feel frightened about him.' (p. 68)

Sample answers [pp. 68–71]

1. Student A: 1 - mid level; Student B: 2 - lower level

3. Student A: 2 - mid level; Student B: 1 - high level

5 Paragraph 1: *In this scene, Conan Doyle depicts the pursuit of Jonathan Small as particularly exciting – with the 'fierce energy' of the boat's overworked engines implying violent or aggressive movement, and also by including the sensory description of the creaking boat. This implies that the boat is at risk of breaking up and sinking altogether.*

Paragraph 2: *Watson's response to the chase is at first that of exhilaration as he admits the chase gives him 'a wild thrill'. However, Tonga who initially appears as a 'huddled bundle upon the deck', terrifies Watson as he transforms to a 'savage, distorted creature'. This links to the use of the word 'savage' that Watson first used for Tonga earlier in the novella, reflecting Victorian attitudes of fear towards people from other cultures.*